PRACTICAL ELECTRONIC BUILDING BLOCKS

CW00687079

ALSO BY THE SAME AUTHOR

PRACTICAL ELECTRONIC BUILDING BLOCKS

BOOK 2

by
R. A. PENFOLD

BERNARD BABANI (publishing) LTD
THE GRAMPIANS
SHEPHERDS BUSH ROAD
LONDON W6 7NF
ENGLAND

Although every care has been taken with the preparation of this book, the publishers or author will not be held responsible in any way for any errors that might occur.

© 1983 BERNARD BABANI (publishing) LTD

First Published — May 1983

British Library Cataloguing in Publication Data
Penfold, R. A.
    Practical electronic building blocks.
    Bk. 2
    1. Electronic circuits
    I. Title
    621.381513   TK7867

    ISBN 0 85934 093 7

Printed and bound in Great Britain by Cox & Wyman Ltd, Reading

Preface

Like "Practical Electronic Building Blocks Book 1", this book is designed to provide a number of useful electronic circuits which can be used to help readers put together their own projects. Whereas "Book 1" provided circuits that were generally concerned with generating signals of some kind (oscillators, noise and current generators, etc.), this book is mainly concerned with circuits that process signals. The two obvious topics of amplifiers and filters account for a large part of this publication, but comparators, Schmitt Triggers, and other signal processing circuits are also covered.

In keeping with "Book 1", all circuits are tried and tested with circuit values and other necessary practical information being provided, together with details of how to modify circuits to suit your particular needs. For example, component values for filters are given for a particular frequency, but details of how to determine the values for other operating frequencies are provided, and only simple calculations are involved.

"Book 1" and "Book 2" do not overlap one another, and have been designed to complement rather than compete with each other. Although there are a number of specialised circuits which are not covered in either publication, between them these books cover virtually every type of oscillator, filter, amplifier, etc. that the average electronics enthusiast is likely to need.

R. A. Penfold

CONTENTS

Chapter 1

AMPLIFIERS

Practically every electronic project incorporates an amplifier stage or stages, and many projects are little more than a collection of amplification stages of various types. There are actually a great many types of amplifier, such as precision DC types, relay drivers, low noise audio, and so on. Audio amplifiers are the most common type in electronic projects and consequently we will consider these at some length. However, other types such as DC and voltage controlled amplifiers will also be considered.

Single Transistor Amplifier

For a great many applications a simple single stage amplifier is all that is required, and Figure 1 shows the circuit diagram of a very useful and simple single transistor amplifier. This is a basic common emitter stage using a single bias resistor (R1) and collector load resistor R2. C1 is the input coupling capacitor and C2 provides DC blocking at the output.

The voltage gain of the circuit is approximately 150 times, the input and output impedances are about 8k and 4k7 respectively, and the -3dB points of the circuit are at less than 20Hz at the low frequency end and around 100kHz at the high frequency limit. The wideband noise output of the circuit is only about 200μV or so (with the input short circuited), and this represents an excellent signal to noise ratio when the high voltage gain of the amplifier is taken into consideration. The current consumption of the circuit is typically a little under 1mA.

A factor which must be kept in mind when using any amplifier is that the full voltage gain of the circuit is never fully realised in practice. This is due to the source impedance of the circuit or transducer driving the input of the amplifier, and the load impedance connected at the output. For example, if the circuit of Figure 1 was to be fed from a source impedance of 16k, this 16k and the 8k input impedance of the amplifier effectively form a potential divider circuit, and the signal is

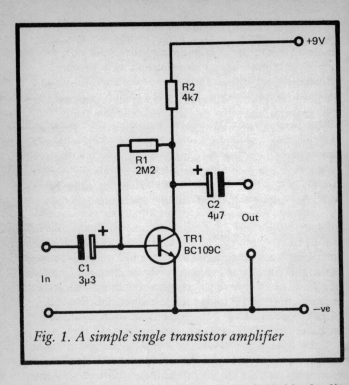

Fig. 1. A simple single transistor amplifier

attenuated by a factor of 3 (16 + 8 = 24, 24 divided by 8 = 3). This would effectively reduce the gain of the amplifier to only about 50 times. A similar potential divider action is produced at the output with the output impedance and load impedance forming the two arms of the potential divider. Thus a load impedance of 4k7 for instance, would effectively reduce the voltage gain of the amplifier by half.

Another important point to note is that although the circuit is capable of an output voltage swing of several volts peak to peak prior to the onset of clipping (the exact figure depending on how accurately the collector voltage of Tr1 is biased to the optimum voltage of 4.5 volts), loading on the output reduces this voltage by the same factor that the voltage gain is effectively decreased.

The specified value for C2 should give good results in most applications, ideally the value of this component should be chosen to suit the input impedance of the circuit driven by the amplifier. It must have a high enough value to prevent low frequencies being significantly attenuated, but it should not have a value that is so high as to give a good response at frequencies well below the limit of the audio band (i.e. well below about 20Hz). A higher value than is really necessary, is not a good idea as it can result in a long wait after switch-on before the capacitors charge to their normal working levels and the circuit starts to function properly. It can also lead to instability due to very low frequency feedback through the supply lines, or "motorboating" as this form of instability is often called.

A value of $4\mu7$ is suitable for load impedances of around 5 kilohms, but for load impedances of substantially less than this it is advisable to increase the value of C2 in proportion to the reduction in load impedance. For example, a load impedance of 1k would require the value of C2 to be increased by a factor of about 5, and a $22\mu F$ component would be suitable since this is the nearest preferred value to the calculated figure of $23.5\mu F$ ($4.7\mu F \times 5 = 23.5\mu F$). Similarly, a higher load impedance enables a proportionately lower value to be used for C2.

Although a supply voltage of 9 volts is specified in Figure 1 the circuit will in fact work quite well using any supply voltage of between about 3 and 20 volts, and the collector voltage of Tr1 will always tend to stabilise at roughly half the supply voltage. Of course, changing the supply voltage does have some effect on the performance of the circuit, the main one being a drop in voltage gain at lower supply voltages, and a small increase in voltage gain at higher supply potentials. The supply current also increases and decreases with the change being roughly proportionate to changes in supply voltage in this case. The maximum peak to peak output voltage prior to clipping also changes approximately in proportion to changes in supply voltage. The other main parameters are little effected by variations in supply voltage.

3

Lower Gain

In many applications the gain of the basic circuit of Figure 1 is excessive, but the gain of the circuit is easily reduced by applying negative feedback. This can be accomplished by simply adding an emitter resistor, as shown in Figure 2.

The voltage gain of the circuit is approximately equal to the collector resistor value (4k7) divided by the emitter resistance, but this emitter resistance includes internal emitter resistance of Tr1 which is about 30 ohms at the collector current used here. If we take a simple example and assume that R3 has a value of 220 ohms, including the internal emitter resistance of Tr1 this gives a total emitter resistance of 250 ohms. 4700 ohms divided by 250 ohms equals 18.8, and the approximate voltage gain of

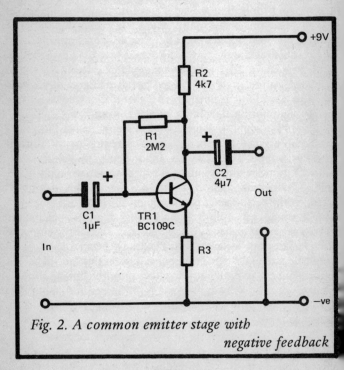

Fig. 2. A common emitter stage with

negative feedback

the circuit is therefore 18.8 times.

In order to calculate the emitter resistor for a given voltage gain requirement it is merely necessary to divide 4700 by the required voltage gain, and then deduct 30 ohms.

The negative feedback introduced by the addition of an emitter resistor has the advantage of reducing noise and distortion in proportion to the fall in voltage gain produced. Another by-product of the negative feedback which can sometimes be helpful is the boost in input impedance that is produced, but there is not a reduction in the output impedance. The input impedance of Tr1 is approximately equal to its current gain multiplied by the emitter resistance (including the internal emitter resistance). However, this is just the input impedance of the transistor and does not take into account the effect of the bias resistor. Although this resistor may seem to be too high in value to have any significant shunting effect on the input impedance of the circuit, the negative feedback effectively reduces the value of this resistor by a factor equal to the voltage gain of the amplifier. In practice this results in the input impedance of the amplifier as a whole being only about half the input impedance of Tr1 alone.

In both Figure 1 and Figure 2 it has been assumed that the output of the circuit connects to a point in the subsequent circuitry that is at the 0V supply potential, or at least at a fairly low voltage. Similarly, it has been assumed that the input connects to a point in the earlier circuitry that is at 0V or very little more than this. If the input connects to a DC potential which is more than about 0.65 volts positive of the 0V rail the polarity of C1 must be reversed, and C2's polarity should be changed if the output connects to a point at a quiescent DC level of more than about half the supply voltage.

The specified value for C1 should give good results, but ideally this should have a value chosen to suit the input impedance of the amplifier in the same way that C2 should have its value chosen to suit the input impedance of the subsequent circuit (as explained earlier).

One final point is that the negative feedback tends to improve the high frequency response of the circuit, and for a circuit having a great deal of feedback the upper -3dB point is likely to occur at a frequency of several Megahertz. This is not of any consequence in true audio applications since even without feedback the amplifier has a response which extends well beyond the upper limit of the audio band. In fact it can be a disadvantage as it can increase the susceptibility of the circuit to stray radio frequency pick-up.

Emitter Follower

As was explained earlier, loading of one stage on another, or loading of a circuit of some kind on a transducer such as a microphone, can produce a large reduction in signal level. Losses due to loading can be substantially reduced using a buffer amplifier, and simple emitter follower buffer circuit is shown in Figure 3.

An emitter follower has 100% negative feedback and therefore only unity voltage gain, but the full current gain of the transistor is realised so that only a small input current is needed to give a comparatively large output current, and the required high to low impedance conversion is thus obtained. It should perhaps be pointed out that an emitter follower stage does not actually give unity voltage gain, but in actual fact gives marginally less than unity gain (about 0.96 being the typical voltage gain obtained). This very small drop in signal level is not usually of any practical significance though.

The input impedance of the circuit is equal to the parallel impedances of R1, R2 and the input impedance of Tr1. These give an input impedance of roughly 100k using the specified values. The output impedance of the circuit is 2k2, but this does not take into account the affect of the source impedance of the input signal. This lowers the output impedance of the circuit to a figure which can be calculated by dividing the source impedance by the current gain of Tr1 (which is about 520 at the collector current used here). In fact the basic 2k2 output impedance of the amplifier is in parallel with the impedance obtained from the calculation detailed above, but in practice the output impedance of the circuit will normally be so low that this 2k2 is of no consequence.

Although the output impedance of the circuit is likely to be

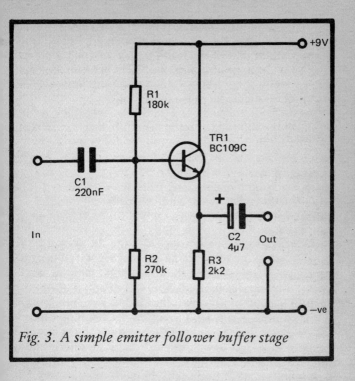

Fig. 3. A simple emitter follower buffer stage

only about 100 ohms or less in a practical situation, and normal loading of the output will not significantly reduce the output signal level of the unit, it is important to bear in mind that the maximum output current of the circuit is equal to the emitter current of Tr1, or about 2mA using the values specified in Figure 3. In other words, trying to provide an output signal of a few volts peak into a load impedance of only about a hundred ohms will not give satisfactory results since the output current capability of the circuit will be inadequate on signal peaks, and clipping will occur. The purpose of a circuit of this type is to match a source impedance of (say) about 10 or 20k to a comparatively low input impedance of (say) about 1 or 2k without producing the massive loss of signal level that would occur using direct connection of the two pieces of equipment.

7

The circuit is not intended to be a power amplifier and will not work as one.

The circuit will work reasonably well on any supply potential of between about 3 volts and 18 volts. The current consumption from a 9 volt supply is about 2mA, and this changes roughly in proportion to alterations in the supply voltage.

Due to the large amount of negative feedback employed in the circuit the noise and distortion levels are both extremely low.

Op. Amp. Buffer

Operational amplifier integrated circuits make an excellent basis for a buffer amplifier, and a simple circuit of this type is given in Figure 4.

100% negative feedback is applied to the circuit by simply coupling the output direct to the inverting input, and there is then unity voltage gain from the non-inverting input to the output. Unlike an emitter follower stage an operational amplifier with 100% negative feedback does give unity voltage gain and not marginally less than unity. R1 and R2 are used to bias the non-inverting input to half the supply potential, and the input impedance of IC1 is so high that it does not significant shunt one of the bias resistors, and these are simply made the same value. At audio frequencies the input impedance of IC1 is so high that it does not have any significant effect on the input impedance of the circuit, and the input impedance is thus approximately equal to the parallel impedance of R1 and R2, or 1.1 Megohms in other words. The input impedance is easily increased or decreased by raising or lowering the value given to R1 and R2, and is simply half the value given to these componer

The current consumption of the circuit is only about 2mA, but the 741C has a class B output stage that can provide output currents of up to about 20mA with a consequent increase in supply current. The output impedance is extremely low (only about 1 ohm) regardless of the source impedance of the input signal.

In one or two respects an operational amplifier buffer stages is inferior to a common emitter stage, and one of these is the

8

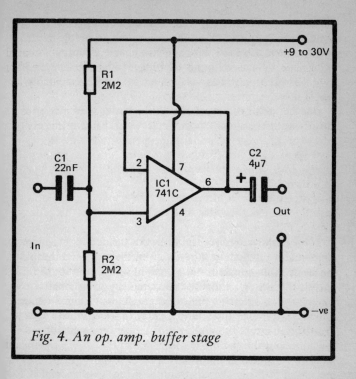

Fig. 4. An op. amp. buffer stage

lower bandwidth of the operational amplifier buffer. The 741C has unity voltage gain at a frequency of about 1MHz, and the circuit therefore ceases to function properly at frequencies above this figure. A common emitter stage will function well at frequencies of many Megahertz. In most applications the bandwidth is not of great importance, and 1MHz is quite sufficient, but a more modern equivalent of the 741C such as the LF351 (4MHz) or CA3140E (4.5MHz) can be used where a wider bandwidth is called for. These more recent operational amplifier devices also have a higher slew-rate than the standard 741C device.

The output voltage swing of an emitter follower (assuming that the output is not heavily loaded) is virtually equal to the supply voltage, but an operational amplifier normally has an output stage which only permits the output voltage swing to reach about 4 volts less than the supply voltage before clipping occurs. There are a few devices which enable an output voltage swing almost equal to the supply voltage to be obtained, and the CA3140E (which has a class A output stage incidentally) is one of these.

Another point to keep in mind is that an operational amplifier buffer stage has a slightly higher noise level than an emitter follower stage unless a special and expensive ultra-low noise device is used. It is probably better to use an emitter follower stage in cases where optimum noise performance is of primary importance.

Hum Filtering

Both the emitter follower and operational amplifier stages have good imunity to hum or other noise on the supply lines provided this noise is not coupled to the input in some way. In the basic circuits of Figures 3 and 4 the bias circuits provide a path from the supply lines to the input of the amplifiers. Where hum or other noise on the supply lines is likely to be a problem it is recommended that the slightly modified arrangements shown in Figures 5 and 6 should be used.

If we consider the circuit of Figure 5 first, this is the same as the circuit of Figure 3 apart from the inclusion of a simple decoupling network (R1 and C1) which removes noise from the bias circuit's supply. With the exception of the improved immunity to hum on the supply lines the circuit has a performance which is not significantly different to that of the original circuit.

The buffer circuit of Figure 6 uses R1 and R2 to produce a bias voltage nominally equal to half the supply potential, and C1 removes any noise present on this bias voltage. R3 couples this bias potential to the non-inverting input of IC1, and there is no significant voltage drop through R3, even if it has a very high value, due to the extremely high input impedance of IC1. The input impedance of the circuit is equal to the value of the component used in the R3 position, and the value of this component can obviously be varied to give any desired input impedance within reason.

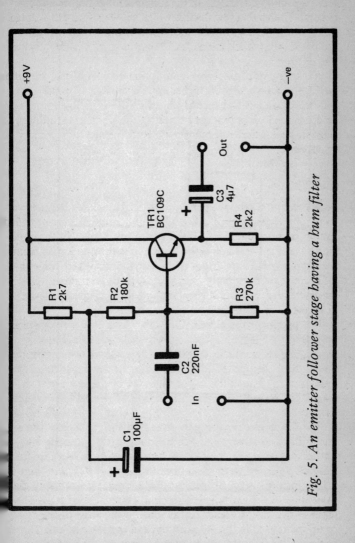

Fig. 5. An emitter follower stage having a hum filter

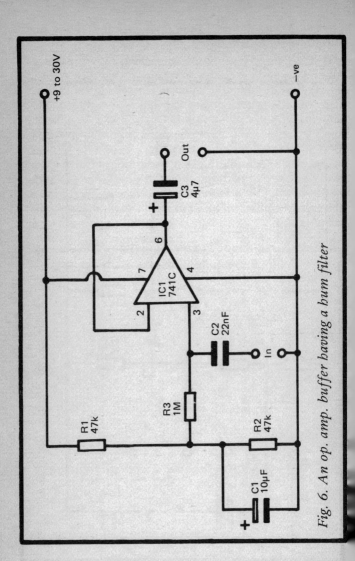

Fig. 6. An op. amp. buffer having a bum filter

12

DC Buffering

It is often necessary to drive a comparatively low impedance
load from a medium or high impedance source, such as driving
a relay from the output of an operational amplifier or CMOS
logic integrated circuit. An emitter follower stage is just as
useful in DC applications, such as this, as it is in AC buffering
applications. Figure 7 shows the circuit diagram of two simple
DC emitter follower buffer amplifiers.

The first of these uses an NPN transistor and switches the
load on when the input voltage is at or close to the positive supply
rail, and switches it off when the input potential is at or near
the negative supply voltage. The input current drawn by the
circuit is equal to the current taken by the load divided by the

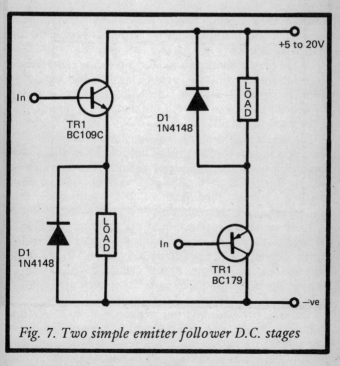

Fig. 7. Two simple emitter follower D.C. stages

13

current gain of Tr1 (which is about 500 or so), and the input current is therefore likely to be very low at only about $100\mu A$ or less.

An important point to bear in mind is that the BC109C has a maximum current rating of 100mA, and a maximum dissipatio of 300mW, and care must be exercised to ensure that neither of these ratings are exceeded. If necessary a device having higher ratings and fitted with an adequate heatsink must be used. Of course, with high output currents the input current requirement increases, but this can be overcome if necessary by using a Darlington device for Tr1. The TIP122 device, for example, has a typical current gain of 5000 at a collector current of 2 amps, a maximum dissipation of 65 watts, a maximum collector current rating of 5 amps, and a V_{CEO} max. of 100 volts. Using an ordinary transistor in the emitter follower mode there is a voltage drop of about 0.65 volts or so from the input to the output, but note that this figure is approximately doubled for a Darlington device.

D1 is a protection diode which suppresses the high reverse voltage that can be produced across a highly inductive load (such as a relay coil) as it is switched off. Of course, if the load is a non-inductive type such as a LED indicator it is not necessary to include D1.

The second emitter follower buffer circuit uses a PNP transistor, and the load is switched on with the input at approximately the negative supply potential, and is switched off with the input at or close to the positive supply voltage. For a high power version of the circuit a TIP127 (the complementary device to the TIP122) is suitable.

There are a few situations where a DC buffer amplifier is required that has an extremely high input impedance, an output current capability of a few milliamps, and no significant DC shift from the input to the output. This can be accomplished using an operational amplifier buffer stage such as the one show in Figure 8.

This is simply a non-inverting amplifier with 100% negative feedback from the output to the inverting input so that the circuit has unity voltage gain. The CA3140E device specified for ICI has a PMOS input stage which gives an input impedance

14

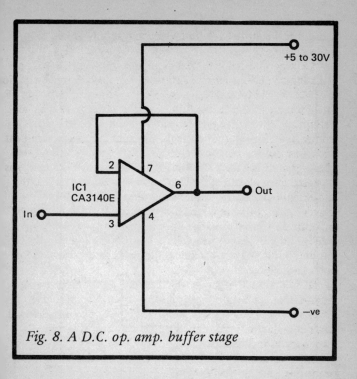

Fig. 8. A D.C. op. amp. buffer stage

of about 1.5 million Megohms, and the circuit therefore places no significant loading on the signal source. The class A output stage of the CA3140E enables the output of the amplifier to go within a few millivolts of the negative supply rail, which is an extremely useful feature in many applications of this type of circuit.

Audio Operational Amplifiers

Some operational amplifiers are primarily designed for use in audio frequency amplifiers despite the fact that these devices were originally designed for use as DC amplifiers. An operational amplifier of this type is the LF351, and Figure 9 shows a simple amplifier circuit which is based on this device. Operational

15

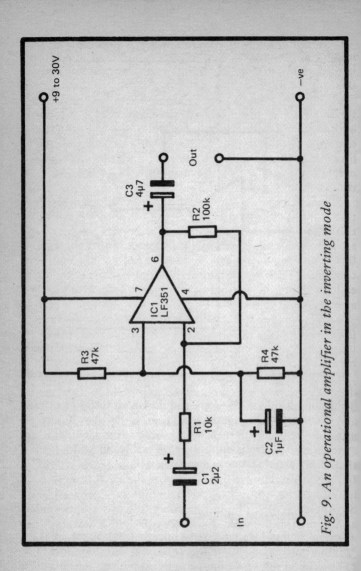

Fig. 9. An operational amplifier in the inverting mode

16

amplifiers can be used in two basic modes of amplification; the inverting mode and the non-inverting one. This circuit is for an inverting amplifier (we will consider a non-inverting amplifier shortly).

R3 and R4 are used to bias the non-inverting input (and also the output) to approximately half the supply voltage. C2 filters out any hum or other noise which might otherwise be coupled to the non-inverting input of IC1 from the supply lines via the bias circuit. This also removes any stray feedback from the output of the amplifier to the non-inverting input and thus reduces the risk of instability.

R1 and R2 are a negative feedback circuit which determine the input impedance and voltage gain of the circuit. By giving these two components the appropriate values it is possible to set both these parameters with a high degree of accuracy, and this makes operational amplifier based circuits (or discrete circuits using similar techniques) ideal for use where it is essential to be able to set the gain and input impedance reliably and consistently.

The input impedance is equal to the value given to R1, and the voltage gain is equal to R2 divided by R1, or ten times using the specified values for these components. C1 and C3 are merely DC blocking capacitors.

Obviously R1 and R2 can be given values to set almost any desired input impedance and voltage gain. However, there are definite limitations on the voltage gain that can be obtained, and to a lesser extent on the input impedance that can be achieved in practice.

If we take the voltage gain first, it must be borne in mind that the gain-bandwidth product of the LF351 device is 4MHz. In other words, the maximum frequency the amplifier must handle multiplied by the voltage gain of the amplifier must be no more than 4MHz. For an amplifier that must cover the full audio band (which extends from about 20Hz to 20kHz) the maximum voltage gain that can be used is clearly 200 times (20kHz multiplied by 200 equals 4MHz). In most cases the LF351 will be able to provide sufficient voltage gain using a single stage of amplification, but two stages connected in series can be used where additional voltage gain is needed.

17

In theory there is no limitation on the input impedance that can be achieved using a circuit of this type, but in practice there is the problem of obtaining resistors of sufficiently high value, especially in cases where a combination of high voltage gain and high input impedance are required. For instance, a circuit having an input impedance of 10 Megohms and a voltage gain o 100 times would require R1 to have a value of 10 Megohms, an R2 to have a value of 1000 Megohms. This is clearly not a practical proposition, and in cases of this type it is better to use a low gain buffer stage to give the high input impedance, and a separate high gain stage to step-up the voltage gain to the desire figure.

Problems can arise with this type of circuit due to the input capacitance of the operational amplifier effectively making the negative feedback, to a degree, frequency selective, so that unwanted peaks or dips in the frequency response are produce This is only really likely to be a problem in circuits that are use to provide low voltage gain and a high input impedance, and the result is normally a roughly doubling in gain at a frequency of a few tens of kilohertz with the response falling away at frequencies above the peak. Where low gain and high input impedance are needed it is better to use a non-inverting amplifi since a low impedance feedback network can then be used, and the input capacitance of the operational amplifier becomes insignificant.

Bearing in mind the limitations mentioned above, the appropriate values for R1 and R2 are easily calculated. R1 is simply given the nearest preferred value to the required input impedance, and then this figure is multiplied by the required voltage gain to give the value of R2 (and again the nearest preferred value must be chosen).

Non-Inverting Amplifier

The circuit of an operational amplifier used in the non-invertin mode is shown in Figure 10. R3 and R4 bias the non-inverting input of IC1 to about half the supply voltage with R5 being us to couple this bias voltage to IC1. C2 decouples any hum or o electrical noise on the supply lines so that it is not fed to the

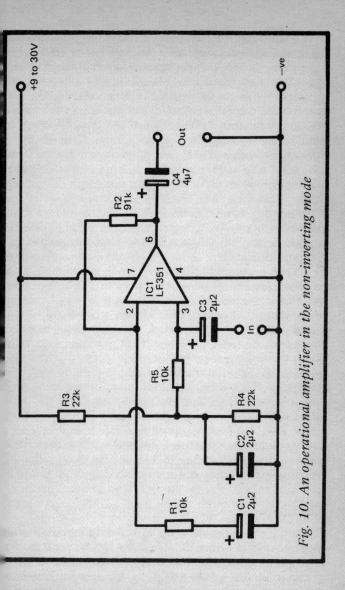

Fig. 10. An operational amplifier in the non-inverting mode

19

input of the amplifier. The value of R5 is equal to the required input impedance of the amplifier, and C2 provides DC blocking at the input (and should have its value chosen to suit the input impedance of the circuit).

R1 and R2 are the negative feedback network, and the volta gain of the circuit can be calculated by first adding the values o R1 and R2, and then dividing this figure by the value of R1. T specified values give a voltage gain of just over 10 times. In theory the values given to R1 and R2 can be any two that have the correct ratio to give the desired voltage gain, but in practice it is not a good idea to have low values that will heavily load th output of the operational amplifier, or to have high values that would result in a far from flat frequency response due to the input capacitance of IC1. In practice it is therefore advisable to have the total value through R1 and R2 at something in the region of 25 to 100k.

In order to choose suitable values for R1 and R2 first decide on a value for R2, and any value of a few tens of kilohms shoul do. Then divide this by one less than the required voltage gain to find the correct value for R1. The nearest preferred value to the calculated figure is the used. C1 is a DC blocking capacitor which gives the circuit 100% negative feedback and unity volta gain at DC so that the circuit is biased properly. At audio frequencies it must not add significantly to the impedance provided by R1, and the correct value is calculated in the same way as the value of the input and output coupling capacitor values are obtained.

The distortion performance of the LF351 is extremely good with the distortion level being only about 0.02% provided the output is not heavily loaded, the circuit is not driven into clipp and the amplifier is not used at very high gain levels. If used a fairly high voltage gains the distortion performance does reduc at high audio frequencies, although the distortion level is still likely to be less than 0.1%.

The noise performance of the LF351 is also extremely good with an output noise level of only about $500\mu V$ even if the amplifier is used at a high voltage gain of one hundred times.

One point that must be emphasized is that although in theo it is perfectly satisfactory to have a non-inverting amplifier wit an input impedance of (say) 5 Megohms and a voltage gain of one or two hundred times, and the LF351 is quite capable of achieving these performance figures, in a practical situation it is highly unlikely that such a circuit could be made to operate satisfactorily. The problem is simply that there would inevitably be a certain amount of stray feedback from the output of the amplifier to the input, and as these two points are in-phase it is almost certain that instability would occur with the circuit breaking into oscillation. It is therefore better to use two stages of amplification with the first giving the high input impedance and the second providing the voltage gain. This enables better separation to be obtained between the input and output so that stray feedback can be reduced to an insignificant level. It is also a good idea to have the second stage of amplification of the inverting type so that the input and output of the amplifier as a whole are then out-of-phase, and any stray feedback will therefore be of the negative variety. This will not cause instability, but will simply result in a small reduction in the high frequency gain of the amplifier.

DC Amplifiers

Operational amplifiers are primarily intended for use in DC amplifiers, as was pointed out earlier, and the same two basic modes of operation are used for DC amplification. However, dual balanced supplies are used with a central 0V earth rail so that the output of the operational amplifier can go right down to the earth potential, and can even go negative with respect to earth.

Figure 11 shows the inverting DC amplifier mode and Figure 12 shows the non-inverting DC amplifier configuration. Taking Figure 11 first, the non-inverting input of IC1 is biased direct to the earth rail so that the quiescent output voltage of the output is the earth rail potential. R1 and R2 are the negative feedback network which set the input impedance and voltage gain of the circuit, just as for the audio inverting amplifier circuit. The DC blocking capacitors at the input and output are obviously omitted.

In the non-inverting circuit R1 and R2 set the voltage gain

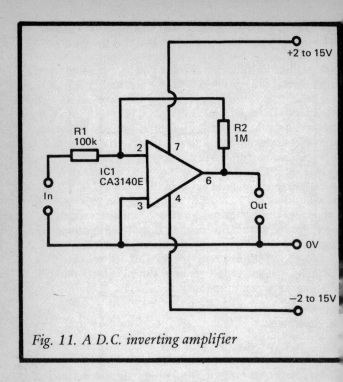

Fig. 11. A D.C. inverting amplifier

of the circuit, just as in the case of the audio non-inverting amplifier, but there is, of course, no DC blocking capacitor in series with R1 (or at the input and output of the circuit). The non-inverting input of IC1 is biased to the 0V rail by R3, and this also sets the input impedance of the amplifier. In many applications the input of the amplifier will always be connecte to a signal source and R3 will be unnecessary unless it is essential for the amplifier to have a particular input impedanc for some reason. With R3 omitted the input impedance of the amplifier is extremely high indeed, but reduces somewhat at high frequencies due to the input capacitance of IC1.

In theory the two inputs and output of the operational amplifier should all be at precisely the 0V supply potential, ar this is true of both amplifying modes. Practical operational

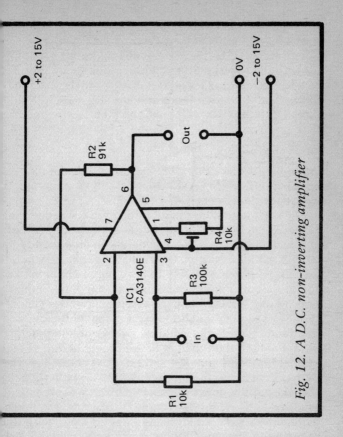

Fig. 12. A.D.C. non-inverting amplifier

amplifiers are not perfect though, and small offset voltages of
usually only a few millivolts are present in the circuit. This can
result in the output of the circuit not being at quite the 0V
supply voltage under quiescent conditions, and if the amplifier
is used at a high voltage gain the output can drift several hundred
millivolts away from the correct level. This is caused by the offset
voltage being multiplied by the voltage gain of the amplifier.

Operational amplifiers usually have provision for an offset
null control which can be adjusted to give a quiescent output
voltage of zero, and R4 of Figure 12 is an offset null control.

An offset null control can be added to the circuit of Figure 11 using a potentiometer of the same value and the same method of connection. This type of offset null control is suitable for use with other operational amplifiers such as the LF351, 741C etc., but there are some that use a different arrangement and these are mostly devices which have an external compensation capacitor (such as the 748C and CA3130T).

Single Supply DC Amplifiers

As the output of the CA3140E (and certain other operational amplifiers such as the CA3130T incidentally) is capable of operating right down to within a few millivolts of the negative supply rail it is sometimes possible to dispense with one of the supply rails in DC amplifier applications. A simple non-inverti amplifier of this type is shown in the circuit diagram of Figure 13. R1 and R2 set the voltage gain of the circuit in the usual way and R3 (if required) sets the input impedance of the circ Ideally the output load should connect between the output terminal of IC1 and the negative supply rail (which will norm be the case), since a load between the output of IC1 and the positive supply rail will tend to increase the minimum output voltage of IC1. The output of IC1 will not go as close to the positive supply rail as it does to the negative one, and a versio of the circuit having the positive supply as the earth rail rathe than the negative supply as earth is unlikely to give satisfacto results.

An inverting DC amplifier having a single supply rail is sho in the circuit diagram of Figure 14. While this may at first ap to be of little practical use since it will only function with the input taken below the negative supply rail, it can sometimes b useful. Obviously preceeding circuitry cannot provide a suita input signal without the addition of a negative supply, makin the circuit effectively a conventional dual rail type. However the circuit can be used in an application such as a high resista voltmeter where the input signal will be provided by a comple separate circuit, and the input signal can be connected so that is of the correct polarity.

Figure 15 shows a useful variation on the basic single rail

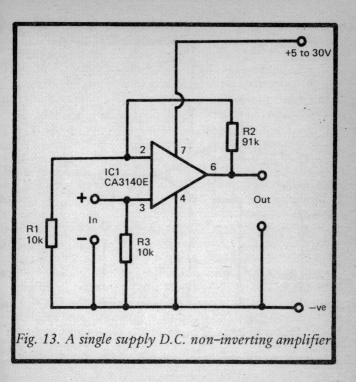

Fig. 13. A single supply D.C. non-inverting amplifier

inverting DC amplifier. This type of circuit is useful for applications where an input signal from perhaps a light or temperature sensing circuit will vary from (say) 1 volt to 1½ volts, and this must be converted to an output of perhaps 0 to 5 volts to drive a meter circuit. With R3 adjusted to give an output voltage of zero with the input voltage at 2 volts, taking the input voltage steadily down to 1.5 volts causes the output to increase by an amount ten times greater than the reduction in input potential (the voltage gain of ten times being set by the values of R1 and R2). Thus the 0.5 volt reduction in the input voltage gives a rise in the output voltage from zero to 5 volts, as required.

One point that should be noted though, is that this is an inverting amplifier and the output should be set at zero with

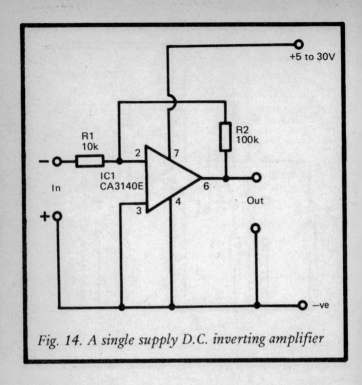

Fig. 14. A single supply D.C. inverting amplifier

the input potential at its maximum level. The output voltage then rises as the input voltage falls. The input circuitry must therefore be designed to give an input voltage that falls as temperature, light level (or whatever) increases, and this is not usually difficult to arrange in practice.

Ultra Low Noise

The device specified for the operational amplifier based audio frequency circuits described earlier is the LF351, and this has a good noise performance as has been pointed out already. However, for very critical applications in this respect there are devices which have a substantially lower noise level, and a useful device of this type is the NE5534A bipolar operational amplifier

26

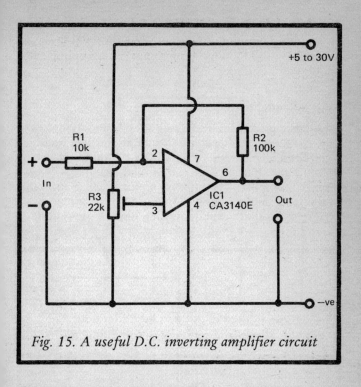

Fig. 15. A useful D.C. inverting amplifier circuit

This can be used in exactly the same way as the LF351, but gives increased bandwidth and lower noise. The gain bandwidth product of the NE5534A is 10MHz which compares to 4MHz for the LF351.

The NE5534A has an input bias current requirement which is considerably higher than that of the JFET input stage of the LF351, and this might cause the output bias voltage to drift significantly away from half the supply potential if very high bias resistor values are employed with this device. However, this may not be significant as the NE5534A is only likely to be used to amplify low level signals and is not likely to require a large output voltage swing, but it is a point which should be kept in mind in applications where the circuit is powered from a fairly low voltage supply and the output could be as large as a few volts peak to peak.

The current consumption of the NE5534A is a little higher than that of the LF351 incidentally, but it is still only about 4mA.

Voltage Controlled Amplifiers

Many audio processing circuits such as expanders, compressors, and certain musical effects units require an amplifier whose voltage gain can be varied by means of a control voltage. Although the MC3340P voltage controlled amplifier is by no means a new device, it is extremely useful for use in applications of this type, and as can be seen from the circuit diagram of Figure 16 this device requires very few discrete components.

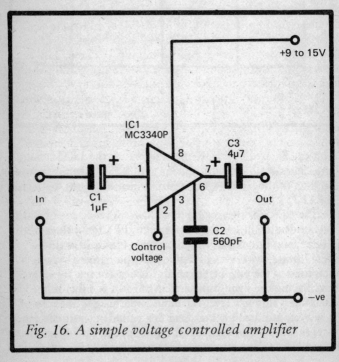

Fig. 16. A simple voltage controlled amplifier

C1 and C3 are input and output coupling capacitors respectively, and C2 attenuates the high frequency response of the circuit to prevent instability. The upper frequency response of the circuit still extends well beyond the upper limit of the audio band though.

The control voltage is applied to pin 2 of IC1, and a potential of about 3.5 volts or less gives a voltage gain of about 13dB (i.e. just over 4 times). The voltage gain falls by about 20dB (ten times) with a control voltage of 4.7 volts, 40dB (100 times) with a control voltage of 5.2 volts, 60dB (1000 times) with a control potential of 5.5 volts, and 80dB (10000 times) with a control potential of 5.8 volts. The maximum attenuation available is about 90dB (30000 times) with a 6 volt control potential. It is also possible to use a resistance from pin 2 to the negative supply rail to control the gain of the circuit, and this resistance should have a value of about 4 kilohms or less in order to give the full 13dB voltage gain of the MC3340P. Reductions in voltage gain of 20, 40, 60 and 80dB are achieved with approximate control resistance of 8k8, 12k, 16k5 and 25k respectively. The maximum attenuation of about 90dB is achieved using a control resistance of about 35k.

The MC3340P can handle a maximum input voltage of about 500mV RMS, and the total harmonic distortion is normally less than 1%, although it does rise somewhat higher than this if the circuit is used with high input levels and at high levels of attenuation.

The MC3340P can sometimes be a little awkward to use due to the fairly low input impedance at the control input, but this can easily be overcome using a buffer amplifier ahead of this input, as shown in Figure 17.

R1 gives the full 13dB voltage gain of the MC3340P under quiescent conditions, but the voltage gain can be reduced by taking the base of Tr1 to a suitable potential. Note that the voltage fed to the base of Tr1 needs to be about 0.6 volts or so above the control voltage required at pin 2 of IC1 due to the voltage drop through Tr1. The input impedance to the base of Tr1 is a few hundred kilohms, and this should be more than adequate. However, if an even higher input impedance is required this can be obtained by using an operational amplifier unity

29

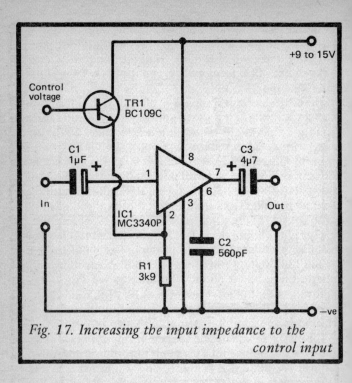

*Fig. 17. Increasing the input impedance to the
control input*

gain buffer stage ahead of the control input of IC1. Of course,
with an operational amplifier buffer stage there is no voltage
drop from the input of the buffer stage to the output. R1 wou[_]
not be necessary if an operational amplifier buffer stage is used.

Transconductance Amplifier

A transconductance operational amplifier makes a good basis f[o]
a voltage controlled amplifier, and Figure 18 shows the circuit
diagram of a VCA using the CA3080E transconductance device
This type of amplifier is quite different to a normal operation[al]
amplifier, and it is the output current rather than the output
voltage that is proportional to the differential input voltage.
This type of amplifier can be made to operate as a voltage

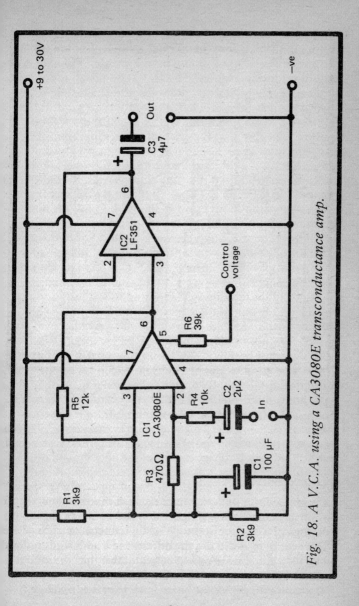

Fig. 18. A V.C.A. using a CA3080E transconductance amp.

31

amplifier however, and it is merely necessary to add a load resistor at the output so that the output current flowing in this resistor produces a proportional output voltage. The output impedance is quite high and a buffer stage is therefore needed at the output in normal use. R5 is the load resistor and IC2 is used as a simple unity gain buffer stage.

In order to use a transconductance amplifier as a VCA it must be used open loop (i.e. without any negative feedback), since any negative feedback would attempt to stabilise the voltage gain of the circuit at a certain level, and would obviously prevent the circuit from operating properly. R1, R2 and C1 are used to effectively give a central 0V supply rail, and the inverting input of IC1 is biased to this via R3 while the non-inverting input is directly connected to it. The gain of the amplifier is controlled by a current fed to pin 5 of IC1, but as it is normally more convenient to use a control voltage rather than a control current R6 has been added in series with pin 5. Thus the input current is roughly proportional to the applied voltage, and the required voltage control is obtained.

The voltage gain of IC1 is higher than is likely to be needed, and the input impedance at about 470 ohms is rather low. R4 is therefore used to reduce the voltage gain to a more suitable level and boost the input impedance of the circuit by 10k.

With a control voltage of 9 volts the circuit has a voltage gain of approximately 6dB (two times). The gain is reduced by about 6dB, 20dB, 40dB, 60dB and 80dB with control voltages of 4.5 volts, 1.5 volts, 0.65 volts, 0.5 volts and 0.43 volts respecitvely. This may seem to be a strange control characteristic with large voltage changes at one end of the range having little effect on the gain, and small voltage changes at the opposite end of the range having a very large effect on the voltage gain. However, this characteristic can be useful in certain applications, especially in ones associated with electronic music such as envelope shaper

The maximum signal level that can be handled by this circuit is about 1 volt RMS. The output noise level is about 1.5mV at maximum gain, and in this respect this circuit is inferior to those using the MC3340P. With both devices the output noise level reduces as the gain of the circuit is reduced. This circuit also has significantly higher distortion levels than the two circuits

32

described earlier which use the MC3340P. This circuit is therefore not recommended for applications where low noise and distortion levels are important.

Opto-Isolator

An opto-isolator consisting of a LED driving a cadmium sulphide cell makes an excellent basis for a voltage controlled amplifier due to the low distortion provided by the photocell. Figure 19 shows the circuit diagram of a VCA of this type, and this uses an ordinary TIL209 (3mm red) LED driving an RPY58A cadmium sulphide photoresistor. The light output from the LED is aimed straight at the sensitive surface of the photocell using as little spacing between the two as possible, and the photocell must be shielded from light other than that emanating from the LED.

R2 and PCC1 are connected to form a simple attenuator, and with PCC1 in darkness there are only quite small losses through this circuit. IC1 is used as a low gain non-inverting amplifier, and this compensates for the losses through the attenuator so that under quiescent conditions the circuit has approximately unity voltage gain, and acts as a simple buffer amplifier.

If the control voltage to the base of Tr1 is steadily increased, at a potential of about 2.5 volts D1 begins to conduct and produce a light output which reduces the resistance of PCC1. This results in increased losses through the attenuator, and thus also through the circuit as a whole, with a maximum attenuation of over 40dB with the control voltage at the positive supply potential. This gives a more than adequate range for most applications.

The circuit can handle input signal levels of up to about 2 volts RMS with minimal distortion. The input impedance at the control input is around 500 kilohms. An important point to note about this type of circuit is that it has quite a fast attack time of only a few milliseconds at most, but the decay time is quite long. In fact it can take about a second or so for the gain of the circuit to return to maximum if the control voltage is rapidly switched from its maximum level to zero, although the gain will return quite rapidly to a level not far below the maximum

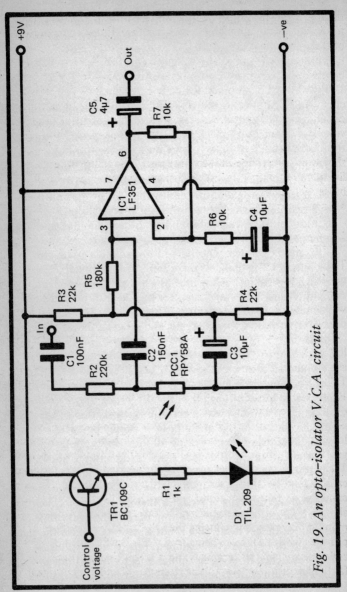

Fig. 19. An opto-isolator V.C.A. circuit

34

figure. This is not usually a disadvantage since it is often necessary for audio control circuits to have attack and decay characteristics of this type anyway.

This type of opto-isolator arrangement is very versatile, and by using PCC1 in the R2 position and using a resistor of about 1k8 in value in the position formerly occupied by PCC1 the circuit provides losses of about 40dB or so under quiescent conditions, with the gain increasing to about unity as the control voltage is brought up to 9 volts. As PCC1 is electrically isolated from the circuit that drives it there is no reason why PCC1 should not be used in the feedback circuit of an amplifier to directly control its gain, rather than using an attenuator and buffer amplifier as in the circuit described here. There is plenty of scope here for those who like to experiment with circuits.

Simple VCA

There are occasions when a very simple VCA is all that is needed, and quite high levels of distortion are acceptable. Applications which fall into this catagory are sound effects which are based on noise, or squarewave signals, or something of this nature where the distortion will not be apparent.

Figure 20 shows the circuit diagram of a simple and admittedly low quality VCA, and this uses an ordinary bipolar transistor as a simple form of voltage controlled resistor. With the base of Tr1 at about 0.5 volts or less Tr1 is cut off and the losses through R1 are those brought about by the input impedance of the output buffer amplifier based on IC1. This amplifier has a certain amount of voltage gain so that it compensates for the losses through R1 and overall gives approximately unity voltage gain. As the control voltage is increased above about 0.5 volts Tr1 begins to conduct between its collector and emitter terminals, causing increased losses through R1. The losses through the circuit as a whole reach about 50dB with the control voltage at about 9 volts. This can be increased to as much as 80dB or more, if necessary, by reducing the value of R2. Of course, Tr1 provides what is far from being true resistance between its collector and emitter terminals and it is this that gives the fairly high distortion level. The circuit can handle input signal

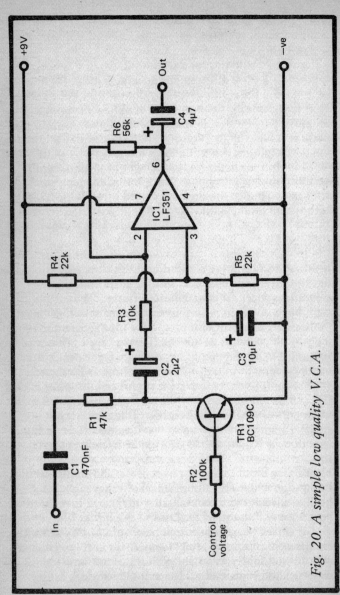

Fig. 20. A simple low quality V.C.A.

36

levels of up to about 2 volts RMS.

Power Amplifiers

Power amplifiers are used in a great many types of project such as radio receivers, intercoms, signal tracers, and guitar amplifiers. Except where fairly high output powers of about 10 watts or more are required, integrated circuit audio power amplifiers are more practical and often cheaper than using a discrete design. Although there are a large number of different audio power amplifier integrated circuits available these days, only a few different types are really needed in order to satisfy most requirements. Here we will consider just four devices which cover most requirements from low voltage low power types to high quality circuits capable of an output power of several watts RMS.

Probably the most popular audio power device in use today is the LM380N integrated circuit, and this popularity is probably due to the high performance and small number of discrete components required by this device. Figure 21 shows the circuit of a simple power amplifier based on an LM380N.

There are actually two inputs to the LM380N; an inverting input at pin 6, and a non-inverting input at pin 2. However, this device is not like an operational amplifier in that it has internal biasing circuitry and a negative feedback circuit that sets the voltage gain of the device at a nominal figure of 34dB (50 times). It is usually better to use the inverting input as this often gives better stability and makes component layout less critical than when using the non-inverting input. The inputs can either be left floating or they can be referenced to the negative supply rail. Thus it is not necessary to use a DC blocking capacitor between volume control VR1 and the inverting input of IC1. Also, the non-inverting input can simply be connected straight to the negative supply rail in order to prevent stray pick-up and feedback to this input.

The circuit will give an output power of 2 watts RMS with a low harmonic distortion level of only about 0.2% or less, and with a 9 volt supply an output power of over 1 watt RMS at low distortion can be produced. The maximum average supply

37

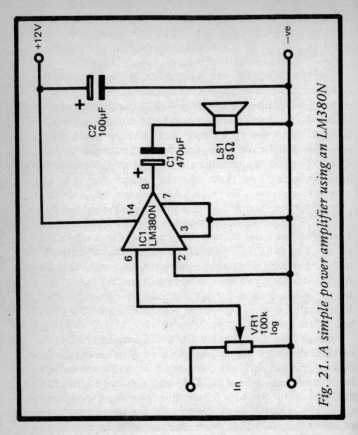

Fig. 21. A simple power amplifier using an LM380N

current is about 250mA using a 12 volt supply, and 180mA using a 9 volt supply. The quiescent supply current is typically 7mA, but can be as high as 25mA.

The circuit can be used with a loudspeaker having an impedance of more than 8 ohms, but the output power decreases in proportion to the increase in speaker impedance. The use of a loudspeaker having an impedance of less than 8 ohms is not recommended. When used with a mains power supply it is beneficial to add a 10μF decoupling capacitor from pin 14 of IC1 to the negative supply (with the positive terminal

38

of the capacitor connecting to pin 14 of course). This increases the ripple rejection of the circuit from only about 7dB to around 40dB, and should substantially reduce the hum level on the output signal if a simple mains power supply is used.

Pins 3, 4, 5, 10, 11 and 12 of the LM380N are internally connected incidentally, and it is only necessary to make a connection to one or other of these. They can be connected to an area of printed circuit track which then acts as a small heatsink, but if the device is only used at output powers of about 2 watts RMS or less this should not be necessary. The LM380N has built-in thermal and overload protection circuitry incidentally.

Low Voltage Amplifier

The LM380N is ideal for many applications where an output power of up to about 2 watts is needed, but it does have one major drawback in that is has a minimum recommended power supply voltage of 8 volts. This obviously permits operation from a 9 volt battery supply, but makes the device unsuitable for applications where a 3 volt or 6 volt battery supply is to be used.

In such cases the amplifier circuit of Figure 22 can be employed, and this is based on the ULN2283B (sometimes just called a 2283) audio power amplifier device. This device only has a non-inverting input and this must be biased to the negative supply rail. In this case it is biased via the volume control VR1. C2 reduces high frequency stray feedback and reduces the risk of instability. The ULN2283B has an internal negative feedback network which sets the voltage gain of the device at a nominal figure of 43dB (about 140 times), and C1 is needed to provide DC blocking in this feedback path. The voltage gain of the circuit might be a little excessive for some applications, and it can be reduced by about 12dB (to about 35 times) using a 100 ohm resistor in series with C1. Lower value resistors can be used to give a smaller reduction in gain.

The circuit will give about 1 watt RMS using a 9 volt supply, about 400mW using a 6 volt supply, and nearly 100mW using a 3 volt supply. Although this last figure may not seem to be

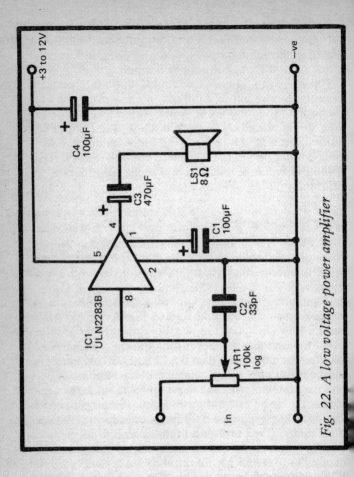

Fig. 22. A low voltage power amplifier

very high, this does in fact give enough volume for applications such as intercoms and small radios, and most miniature loudspeakers are only rated to handle about 100 to 200mW. The quiescent supply current is between 8 and 12mA using a 6 volt supply (10 and 14mA using a 9 volt supply), but the ULN2283 has a class B output stage and the current consumption therefore increases considerably when the circuit is used to provide high volume levels.

Note that pins 2, 3, 6 and 7 of the ULN2283B are internally connected together, and it is only necessary to connect the negative supply rail to one of these.

Low Current Amplifier

A problem when using the two circuits just described with a battery supply is that the quiescent current consumption can be quite high, and the LM380N for example can have a quiescent current consumption of as much as 25mA. For best battery economy a low quiescent current consumption of only a few milliamps is required, and the TBA820M with its quiescent current consumption of only about 4mA is therefore ideal for use with a battery supply, and it will operate with supply voltages as low as 3 volts. There is a slight drawback with this device when compared with the LM380N or ULN2283B in that it requires more discrete components, but the component count is by no means excessive as can be seen from the circuit diagram of Figure 23.

This is another device which needs its input referenced to the negative supply rail, and this biasing is provided by the volume control VR1. Of course, the circuitry driving the amplifier must have DC blocking at the output (or a suitable capacitor must be added at the input of the amplifier) or the DC component on the input signal will upset the biasing of the amplifier. C2 provides supply decoupling for the supply to the input stage of IC1, and this prevents stray feedback over the amplifier due to loading of the supply, and gives increased supply ripple rejection if the circuit is used with a mains power supply. C4 restricts the high frequency bandwidth of the amplifier to reduce the risk of instability, and R3 plus C6 are also needed to aid good stability. R2 and C3 provide boostrapping to the driver stage of the amplifier, and this gives a slight boost in the output power available using a given supply voltage.

This high efficiency is useful when a low voltage supply is used as it enables the circuit to provide an output power of about 150mW into an 8 ohm loudspeaker using a supply potential of just 3 volts. The circuit will actually give about 300mW into a 4 ohm load using a 3 volt supply, although loudspeakers of a

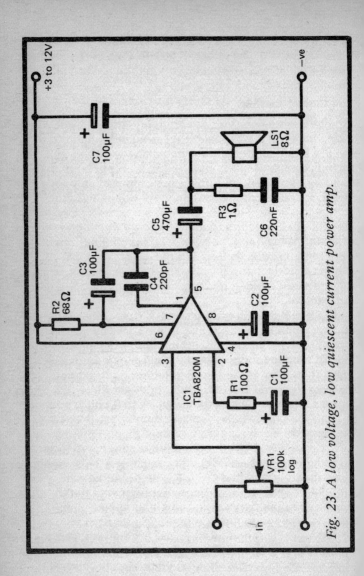

Fig. 23. A low voltage, low quiescent current power amp.

42

suitable impedance might be difficult to obtain. The output power using an 8 ohm speaker is 500mW RMS using a 6 volt supply, about 1 watt RMS using a 9 volts supply, and nearly 2 watts RMS using a 12 volt supply.

The voltage gain of the circuit is controlled by the value given to R1, and as the gain is approximately equal to 6000 divided by the value of R1 (in ohms) the specified value gives a nominal voltage gain of 60 times. The value of R1 can be altered to suit individual requirements, but it is advisable to keep its value between about 27 ohms and 220 ohms. A lower value could cause a serious reduction in output quality and a higher value could result in instability.

6 Watt Amplifier

For output powers of about 6 watts RMS the circuit of Figure 24 is useful. This is based on the TDA2006 device which can be used in much the same way as an operational amplifier. In this circuit it is used as an inverting amplifier with a voltage gain of a little over 26dB (20 times). The voltage gain is set by negative feedback network R1 and R4, just as for an operational amplifier inverting amplifier. In fact, apart from the addition of volume control VR1 it will be apparent that this circuit uses the same configuration as that used in the operational amplifier inverting mode circuit of Figure 9. The input impedance of the amplifier is 22k, but this is shunted by VR1 which reduces the input impedance of the circuit as a whole to 11k at maximum volume.

The TDA2006 can be used in the non-inverting mode if preferred, but the inverting mode seems to give better stability with the component layout consequently being less critical using this mode. The voltage gain and input impedance can be easily modified to suit your requirements, but it is advisable to keep the voltage gain between about 20 and 40dB (10 and 100 times). Using the inverting mode it is not really possible to obtain a high input impedance since R4 would require an impractically high value. The TDA2006 has a bipolar input stage and in order to obtain accurate biasing it is advisable to give R4 a value of no more than about 1 Megohm or so. In the

43

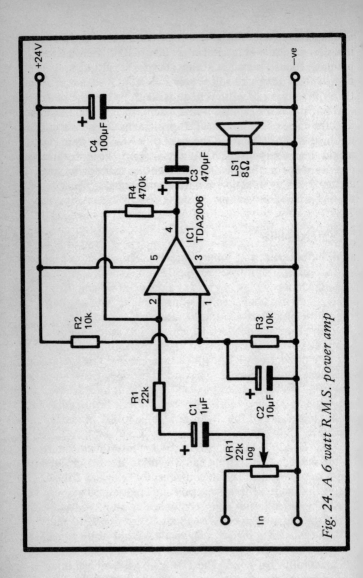

Fig. 24. A 6 watt R.M.S. power amp

44

non-inverting mode a high input impedance can be achieved, but is almost certain to result in violent instability. It is therefore better to use a buffer stage at the input to boost the input impedance to the required figure if an input impedance of more than a few tens of kilohms is required.

The circuit gives a good quality output with a total harmonic distortion level of only about 0.1% or less at output powers of up to about 4 watts. The heat-tab of the TDA2006 must be mounted on a fairly substantial heatsink since the device has to dissipate a few watts when it is used with output powers of around 4 to 6 watts RMS. The heat-tab connects internally to the negative supply pin (pin 3) of the device incidentally. The TDA2006 has both thermal shutdown and output overload protection circuits built-in. The quiescent current consumption of the circuit is about 41mA, but this increases to about 500mA at high volume levels.

Chapter 2

FILTERS

Although there are a great many different types of filter, they really only fall into four main catagories. These are high pass, low pass, bandpass, and notch types. There are many ways of achieving each type of filtering, which is why there appears to be a bewildering variety of filters in use in modern linear circuit. In this chapter we will consider circuits of all four types, and in most cases filters of various levels of performance will be described so that you will (hopefully) be able to choose a filter configuration that precisely suits your needs.

6dB Per Octave Types

The simplest type of filter is a high pass or low pass type that merely consists of one capacitor and one resistor. These two types of filter are shown in Figure 25, and these give an ultimat roll-off rate of 6dB per octave. In other words, a doubling or halving of frequency (as appropriate) results in the output voltage being reduced by 50%.

These circuits rely on the fact that the reactance of a capaci decreases as frequency is increased, and this simple principle is in fact used in all the filters that are described in this publicatio. If we take the low pass filter first, at low frequencies C1 has a reactance which is high when compared with the resistance of R1, and the losses through R1 due to a straight forward potent divider action are therefore very small. At higher frequencies the reactance of C1 falls and eventually reaches a point where i is equal to the resistance of R1, and at this point the losses through the circuit are 6dB. Doubling the input frequency results in a halving of the reactance of C1, and the losses throu the filter are doubled to 12dB. Further doublings of the input frequency cause the reactance of C1 to half, and the losses through the circuit to be doubled (or increased by 6dB in othe words). Thus the ultimate 6dB per octave attenuation rate is achieved. Note though that the roll-off rate is lower than this

46

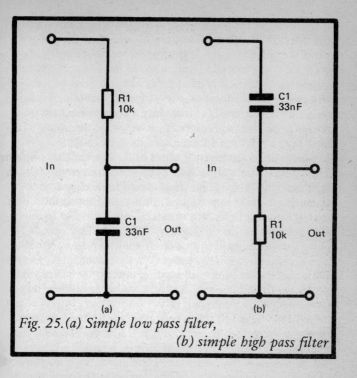

Fig. 25. (a) Simple low pass filter,
              (b) simple high pass filter

at frequencies below the -6dB point, and this type of filter should therefore be said to have an ultimate attenuation rate of 6dB per octave rather than just a 6dB per octave attenuation rate.

The high pass filter works in very much the same way, but it is at high frequencies where the reactance of C1 is low that the circuit produces low losses, and at low frequencies where the reactance of C1 is high in relation to that of R1 that the circuit gives the 6dB per octave roll-off.

The values shown in Figure 25 gives a -6dB point at approximately 1kHz, but the -6dB frequency can be altered by changing the value of C1 or that of R1, or both. Changes in value give an inversely proportional change in the -6dB frequency. For instance, making R1 1k and C1 3n3 would produce a 6dB point at approximately 100kHz.

Circuits of this type look deceptively simple, and this is due to the fact that the cut off frequency obtained and the roll-off rate of the filter are largely dependent on the source and load impedances at the input and output of the filter. For the filter to achieve its theoretical level of performance it must be fed from a source impedance that is very low and have a load impedance that is very high. If we take a couple of extreme examples to demonstrate this point, assume that the circuit of Figure 25(a) is fed from a source impedance of 100k, this source impedance is effectively added to R1 to give a value here of 110k, which would give a -6dB point of less than 100Hz instead of about 1kHz. If the circuit is fed from a low source impedance but a load impedance of 1k is placed across the output, there will obviously be losses of over 20dB due to the potential divider action produced by R1 and the load impedance. C1 would start to significantly increase the attenuation provided by the circuit only when its reactance became comparable to and less than the load impedance. This would be at a frequency of about 10kHz and upwards, and would again seriously effect the performance of the circuit.

In practice circuits of this type are quite often used, but not in the form shown in Figure 25. It would be more common for a simple low pass filter to be in the form of a capacitor connected across the collector load resistor of a common emitter amplifier. Here the cut-off frequency would be determined by the value given to the filter capacitor and the combined impedance of the load resistance and the input impedance of the circuit driven by the amplifier (these two impedances effectively being connect in parallel with one another). Low pass filtering is sometimes added to an operational amplifier circuit such as the one shown in Figure 9 and described earlier. Here the filter capacitor would be added in parallel with R2 so that the amplifier would have increased negative feedback and reduced voltage gain at high frequencies where the filter capacitor would effectively reduce the value of R2 by a substantial amount. The cut-off frequency would then be determined simply by the values of R2 and the filter capacitor.

A high pass filter is often produced by simply using a low value coupling capacitor between two stages so that in effect

48

C1 is the coupling capacitor and R1 is the input impedance of the stage to which it is coupling the signal.

Active Filters

Where a filter having an attenuation rate of more than 6dB per octave is required it is normal these days to use an active circuit. While on the face of it there is no reason why two simple filters of the type shown in Figure 25(a) or (b) should not be connected in series to give a 12dB per octave roll-off rate, in practice loading of the first filter section on the second tends to give problems. A passive 12dB per octave filter tends to have a rather low initial roll-off rate which can result in wanted signals at frequencies just below the cut-off frequency being significantly attenuated, or signals at frequencies not far above the cut-off frequency receiving little attenuation, or a combination of the two, depending on what compromise is used for the cut-off frequency. We are talking in terms of a low pass filter here, but the situation is essentially the same for a high pass type. It then becomes wanted signals just above the cut-off frequency that are attenuated, and (or) signals at frequencies just below the cut-off frequency that receive little attenuation.

With an active filter it is possible to obtain a flat response almost to the frequency where the 12dB per octave roll-off rate commences. Figure 26 shows the circuit diagram of a conventional 12dB per octave low pass filter which uses IC1 as a unity gain buffer amplifier. The cut-off frequency is determined by the values of R3, R4, C2 and C3, with a -3dB point at about 1kHz with the specified values. However, by changing the values of C2 and C3 it is possible to alter the cut-off frequency to practically any desired figure from a few Hertz to about 100kHz. Changes in the values of C2 and C3 produce an inversely proportional shift in the cut-off frequency. For example, a scratch filter with a cut-off frequency of 5kHz could be produced by reducing C2 to 1nF and C3 to 470pF. Obviously where exactly the required values are not available, it is necessary to use the nearest preferred values. It is important to keep C2 at a value which is double or slightly more than double the value of C3. If C2 is slightly lower in value than this the initial roll-off rate

49

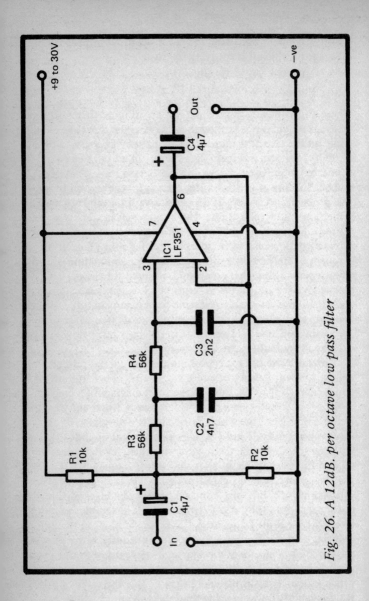

Fig. 26. A 12dB. per octave low pass filter

50

of the filter will be less than optimum, whereas making C2 somewhat too high in value will produce a peak in the response of the filter just below the cut-off frequency.

R1 and R2 are used to bias IC1, and the bias current flows to IC1 via filter resistors R3 and R4. These are placed ahead of the filter resistors so that they do not shunt C3, which would be the case if they were connected direct at the input to IC1. The input impedance of the circuit is about 5 kilohms.

Figure 27 shows the circuit diagram of an active 12dB per octave high pass filter, and this is basically the same as the low pass circuit just described but the resistive and capacitive filter elements have been transposed. R2 and R3 bias IC1, and the combined (parallel) impedance of these acts as one of the resistive filter elements.

The values shown in Figure 27 give a -3dB point at approximately 1kHz, but it is again possible to modify the cut-off frequency by altering the values of the capacitive elements of the filter (C1 and C2). Also as before, changes in value give an inversely proportional shift in the cut-off frequency. Thus, for example, the circuit could operate as a rumble filter in a hi-fi system with a cut-off frequency of around 50Hz by giving C1 and C2 a value of 470nF. Keep these two components at the same value or the performance of the filter will be adversely affected.

High Slope Filters

The circuit of Figure 28 is for a 1kHz low pass filter having a nominal slope of 18dB per octave. This is basically just a 12dB per octave filter of the type already described with an additional filter stage (R3 and C2) added at the input to increase the attenuation rate to 18dB per octave. However, in order to optimise performance the 12dB per octave section of the circuit is designed to have a peak in the response at about 1kHz, and the additional filter is used to counteract this and give a fairly flat response below the cut-off frequency. The overal effect of this is to give a very rapid introduction of the full 18dB per octave attenuation rate, and this type of filter gives extremely good results.

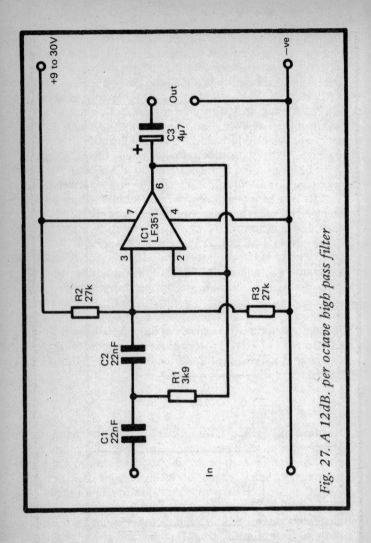

Fig. 27. A 12dB. per octave high pass filter

The operating frequency of the filter, as for the 6 and 12dB per octave types, can be altered by changing the values of the filter capacitors, provided the ratio of their values is not greatly changed (e.g. C2 should always be about ten times higher in value

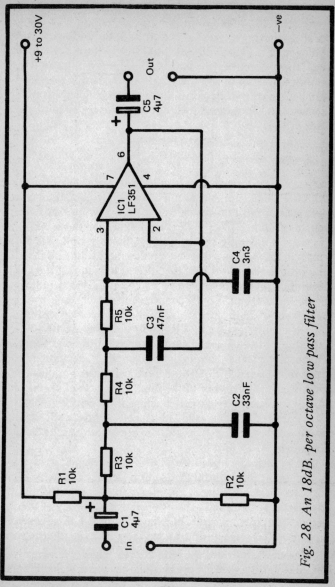

Fig. 28. An 18dB. per octave low pass filter

53

than C4). Figure 29 shows the circuit diagram of the high pass equivalent of the circuit of Figure 28.

For an even higher level of performance the 24dB per octave filter circuits of Figures 30 (low pass) and 31 (high pass) can be used. These effectively use two 12dB per octave filter sections connected in series to give the very high attenuation rate of 24dB per octave (which means that a doubling or halving of frequency, as appropriate, reduces the gain of the circuit by a factor of 16)!

Notch Filter

The purpose of a notch filter is to let most frequencies pass with little hinderance, but to provide a high level of attenuation over a narrow band of frequencies. Figure 32 shows the circuit diagram of a notch filter of the twin T type, and this is really just a passive filter with IC1 being used as a buffer stage at the output of the circuit to ensure that there is minimal loading on the filter proper. R1 and R2 are used to bias IC1, and C1 is a DC blocking capacitor. R3, R4, VR1 and C2 to C5 are the filter components. C4 and C5 are connected in parallel to give a capacitance of 20nF since it is unlikely that a component of this value will be available. VR1 could be replaced with a 9k fixed resistor (which would need to consist of two 18k componen connected in parallel), but in order to obtain a deep notch it is better to use a variable resistor here so that it can be adjusted to optimise the performance of the filter. This type of circuit can provide a very high level of attenuation at the centre of the notch with 80dB being readily obtainable, although VR1 must be adjusted very precisely in order to obtain best results from this circuit.

A drawback of a basic twin T filter in some applications is that it produces significant losses at frequencies well away from the central notch frequency. Typically there is about 10dB of attenuation at twice and half the operating frequency of the circuit. The circuit diagram of a modified twin T filter which is superior in this respect is shown in Figure 33. The filter proper is actually the same as that employed in the previous circuit, but it is included in the negative feedback circuit of an operation

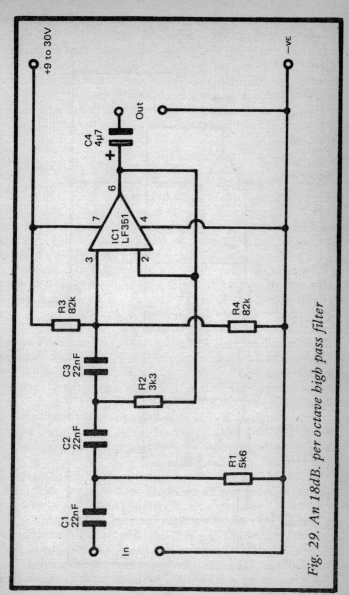

Fig. 29. An 18dB. per octave high pass filter

55

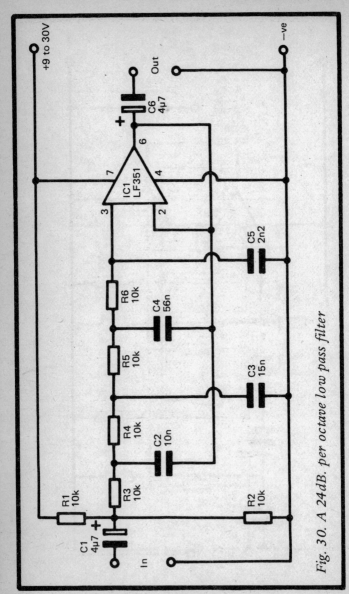

Fig. 30. A 24dB. per octave low pass filter

56

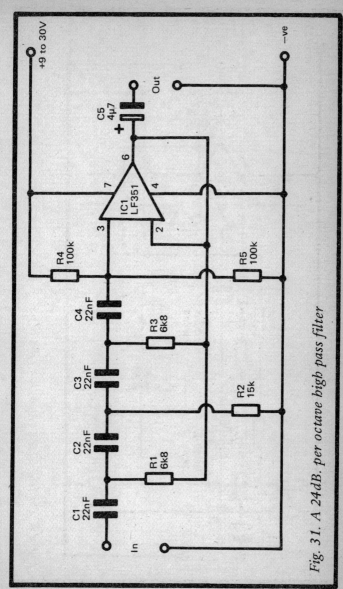

Fig. 31. A 24dB. per octave high pass filter

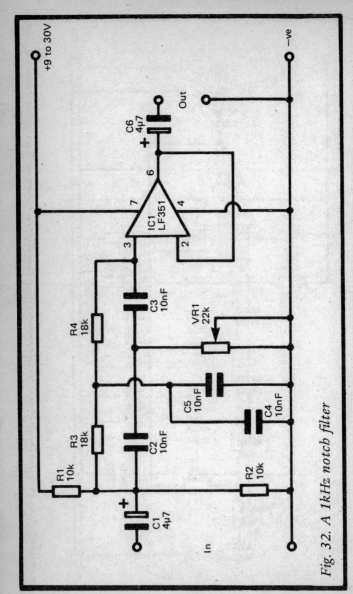

Fig. 32. A 1kHz notch filter

58

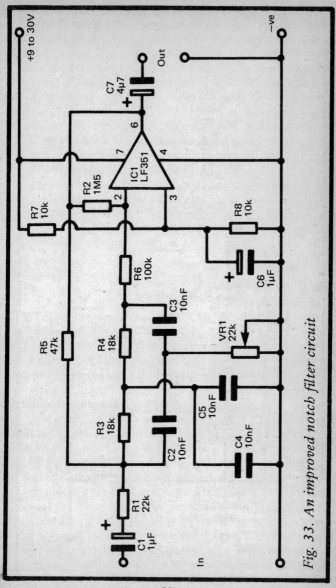

Fig. 33. An improved notch filter circuit

59

amplifier which is used in the inverting mode. The negative feedback tries to flatten the response of the circuit, and therefore reduces losses away from the notch frequency. However, the level of attenuation at the centre of the notch is so high that the negative feedback has no noticeable effect here, and it is still possible to adjust VR1 to give more than 80dB of attenuation. This circuit has losses of only about 1.5dB at twice and half the notch frequency.

The specified filter values give an approximate notch frequency of 1kHz, but the value of C2 to C5 can be altered to give any desired notch frequency from a few Hertz to some tens of kilohertz. As with all the filters described in this book, changes in value give an inversely proportional change in operating frequency. C2 to C5 must all have the same value if the circuit is to function properly, and it is advisable to use components having a tolerance of 5% or less.

Alternative Notch Filter

An alternative notch filter circuit is shown in Figure 34, and this is based on Wien network C3, C4, R3 and R4. IC1 is used as a non-inverting buffer stage which drives one section of the Wien network, and IC2 is used as an inverting buffer stage which drives the other section. At a certain frequency (approximately 1kHz with the specified values) there is zero phase shift through each section of the Wien network, and the out-of-phase signals have a cancelling effect on each other. R6 is adjusted to precisely balance the two signals so that a deep attenuation notch is produced. IC3 is simply used as an output buffer stage.

The performance of this filter is similar to that of the filter circuit of Figure 32, but it does have an advantage that can often be very useful. This is simply that the operating frequency of the filter can be altered by varying the values of the two resistors in the Wien network (R3 and R4), and these two resistors should be of the same value. By using a twin gang potentiometer for these two resistors (with a fixed resistor in series with each gang) it is possible to tune the filter. In fact it can be tuned over a considerable bandwidth if necessary. For example, replacing R3 and R4 with a 220k linear dual gang

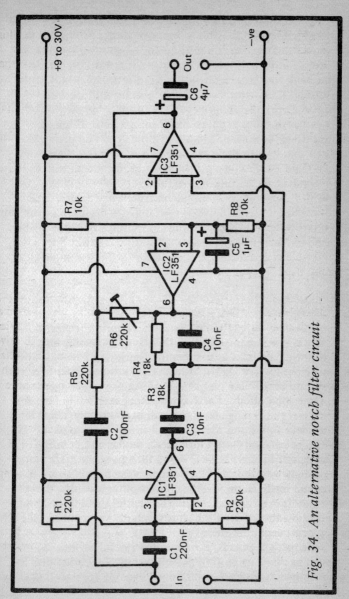

Fig. 34. An alternative notch filter circuit

61

potentiometer with a 1k5 resistor in series with each gang would give a nominal tuning range of less than 100Hz to over 10kHz. Even the ability to have a small tuning range can often be useful or even essential. If it is necessary to notch out a certain frequency, and there is no way of altering the frequency of the input signal that must be removed, it is obviously necessary to bring the operating frequency of the filter to just the right frequency in order to obtain really good results. Using the filter circuit of Figure 32 it can be difficult to find preferred values that give precisely the desired operating frequency, and then there are the component tolerances to contend with anyway. This limits the degree of attenuation that can be obtained using a twin T circuit under these circumstances, and a Wien tunable notch filter is preferable. However, if a high degree of attenuation is not required, or the signal which is to be notched out can be tuned to the centre frequency of the filter, the twin T type is preferable as it is simpler, less expensive, and just as effective under these conditions.

Bandpass Filters

A bandpass filter, as its name suggests, permits frequencies within a narrow band to pass with little attenuation while providing high losses at all other frequencies. A bandpass filter can be produced using the high pass and low pass filter circuits described earlier, and this method of bandpass filtering is used in some applications. For example, suppose an audio filter for some piece of communications equipment is required, and it must have a passband which extends from 250Hz to 3kHz. This could be achieved using a high pass filter having a cut-off frequency of 250Hz and a low pass filter having a 3kHz cut-off frequency with the two filters simply being used in series. It does not really matter too much which filter is used to process the signal first, although a marginally better signal-to-noise ratio will be obtained using the high pass filter at the input and the low pass type at the output.

The method described above is most useful where a flat response over a range of frequencies is required, rather than a filter which is designed to pick out a signal at a certain frequency and attenuate other signals. Where a very narrow bandwidth is required it is better to use a simple bandpass filter of the type shown in Figure 35. The specified values give a centre frequency of approximately 1kHz, but this frequency can be made anything from a few Hertz to about 100kHz by giving C1 and C2

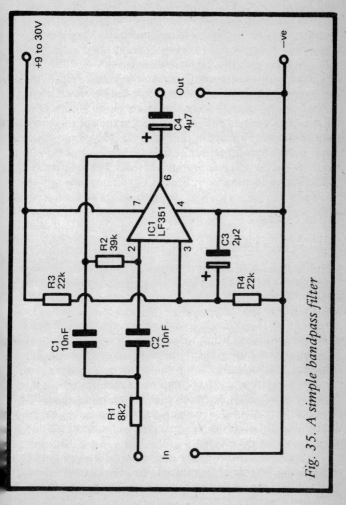

Fig. 35. A simple bandpass filter

suitable values.

A voltage gain of a little over two times is provided at the centre of the filters response, and the response is not particularly sharp with the -6dB points at approximately 500Hz and 2kHz. However, the Q of the circuit can be boosted considerably by reducing R1 to 1k8 and increasing R2 to 180k. This gives a relative attenuation of nearly -20dB at 500Hz and 2kHz, and the voltage gain of the circuit is boosted to about 34dB (50 times). Obviously an attenuator can be used at the input or output of the filter if this voltage gain is not needed.

The circuit must be fed from a low impedance source since the output impedance of the preceding stage is effectively in series with R1 and will reduce the operating frequency of the filter. If necessary a buffer stage (such as the one shown in Figure 4) must be added at the input. The filter can be tuned over a small range of frequencies by replacing R1 or R2 with a variable resistor and fixed resistor in series, but the bandwidth o the circuit will change somewhat as the filter is tuned up and down in frequency (which is why only a limited tuning range is practical).

Narrow Band Filter

The bandpass filter circuit of Figure 36 has a centre frequency of about 1kHz and -20dB points at approximately 850Hz and 1.15kHz. The -40dB points are at approximately 250Hz and 3.2kHz. The gain at the centre of the filters response is about 46dB (200 times).

This narrow bandwidth and very sharp response are obtained using a twin T filter in the feedback network of an operational amplifier used in the inverting mode. At resonance the twin T circuit provides very little feedback and the circuit has a high level of voltage gain, but away from the centre frequency the twin T network provides a comparitively large amount of feedback and gives little or no voltage gain. R5 is used to "dam the response of the twin T circuit slightly, and without this component the circuit would almost certainly break into oscillation. The gain and Q of the filter can be boosted slightly by making R5 slightly higher in value, or the gain and Q can be

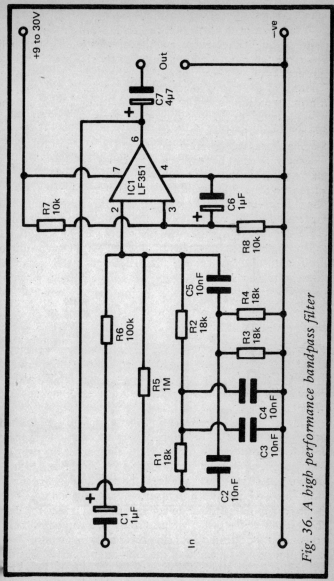

Fig. 36. A high performance bandpass filter

65

reduced by using a lower value for R5.

Tone Controls

Tone control networks can be passive circuits, and a simple tone control network of this type is shown in the circuit diagram of Figure 37. VR1 is the bass control and VR2 is the treble control. Maximum boost is produced with the sliders of these two controls at the tops of the tracks, and maximum cut is produced with them at the bottom ends of the tracks. At 10kHz and 100Hz the maximum cut and boost available is approximately 12dB. The circuit must be fed from a reasonably low impedance source and must have a reasonably high impedance load at the output if it is to function correctly.

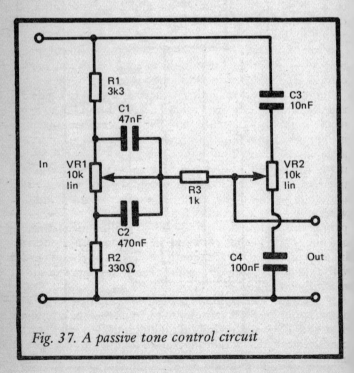

Fig. 37. A passive tone control circuit

A problem with passive tone control circuits is that they have a fairly high insertion loss, and the circuit of Figure 37 is quite typical with losses of about 20dB with the controls set for a flat response. One way of overcoming this problem is to connect the tone control network in the negative feedback loop of an amplifier, as shown in the circuit diagram of Figure 38.

Bear in mind that the gain of the amplifier is reduced at frequencies where the tone control networks provide boost and therefore increased negative feedback. Similarly, the gain of the amplifier is boosted at frequencies where the tone control networks provide cut and there is reduced negative feedback. In other words the controls operate in reverse fashion to the passive version, with the circuit giving maximum bass and treble boost with the sliders of VR1 and VR2 at the bottom end of the tracks, and maximum cut with the sliders at the upper ends of the tracks. In other respects the lift and cut characteristics of the active tone controls are not significantly different to those of the passive circuit.

Rather than losses of about 20dB, the active version of the tone controls provides a voltage gain of nearly 20dB with the controls set for a flat frequency response.

An alternative active tone control circuit is given in Figure 39, and this is based on an operational amplifier used in the inverting mode. In the inverting mode an operational amplifier can be used to provide less than unity voltage gain (which cannot be achieved using a non-inverting amplifier), and this enables the circuit to have unity voltage gain with the controls set for a flat response. Thus when adjusted for boost the circuit does actually provide an increase in gain at the frequencies concerned, and when set for cut the circuit does provide attenuation. The passive tone controls of Figure 37 always provide attenuation, and simply apply more or less attenuation rather than giving true lift and cut. The active tone controls of Figure 38 always provide voltage gain, and simply give more or less voltage gain to give relative boost and cut.

A circuit of the type shown in Figure 39 can often be advantageous since it is very easy to add it into an audio system of some kind. It acts virtually as a buffer amplifier, and if it is connected between two circuits that are compatible with one another it should not introduce any problems of incompatibility.

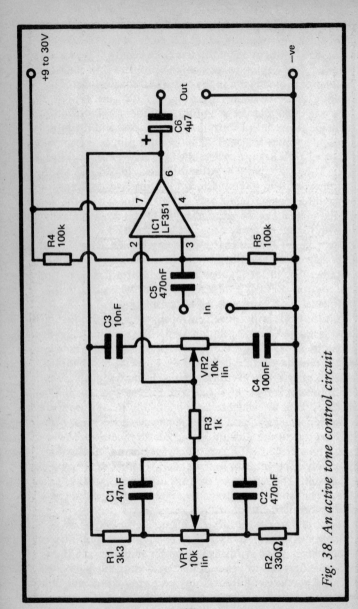

Fig. 38. An active tone control circuit

68

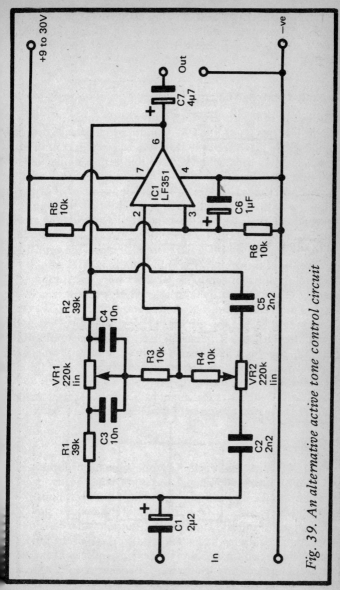

Fig. 39. An alternative active tone control circuit

The control characteristics of this circuit are similar to those of the previous two circuits with maximum lift and cut levels of about 12dB being available at 100Hz and 10kHz (relative to 1kHz).

Voltage Controlled Filter

The circuit of Figure 40 is for a simple voltage controlled filter of the low pass type. The CA3080E transconductance operation amplifier (IC1) is effectively used here as a voltage controlled resistor, and in conjunction with C3 this forms a simple 6dB per octave low pass filter.

With the control voltage at 9 volts IC1 has a fairly low effective resistance, and the -6dB point of the circuit is well beyond the upper limit of the audio frequency spectrum at approximately 50kHz. Reducing the control voltage raises the effective resistance of IC1 and therefore reduces the cut-off frequency of the circuit. The -6dB point is at 1kHz with a control potential of approximately 0.75 volts, and it can be reduced somewhat further if necessary. However, it is advisable not to use a control voltage of much less than 0.75 volts as this could result in the output being cut off completely. Despite this limitation, the cut-off frequency can still be varied over a 100 to 1 range, and this is more than is likely to be necessary in practic applications. Of course, the cut-off frequency range of the circu can be changed by altering the value of C3 if necessary.

At pass frequencies the circuit has a nominal voltage gain of unity. The input impedance of the circuit is about 22k.

Bandpass VCF

Figure 41 shows the circuit diagram of a simple bandpass voltag controlled filter, and although this is not a high quality type it can be useful in applications such as musical effects units and sound effects circuits. One drawback of the circuit is simply th it produces significant amounts of distortion under certain operating conditions, and another is that the Q of the filter changes quite considerably as the centre frequency of the circu is swept upwards through the audio frequency band. At low

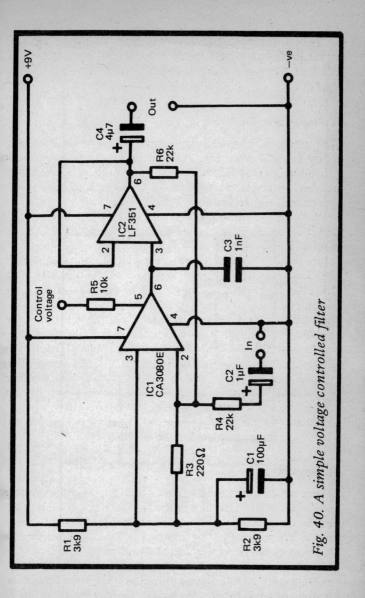

Fig. 40. A simple voltage controlled filter

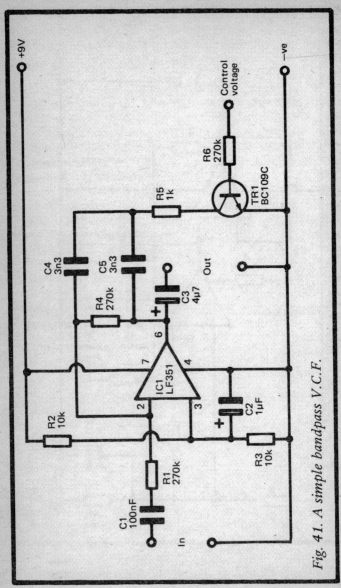

Fig. 41. A simple bandpass V.C.F.

72

frequencies the filter has an extremely low Q with the gain at the centre of the passband being only a few dBs higher than the normal (unity) voltage gain of the circuit. At high frequencies the Q is much higher with a voltage gain of around 20dB at the centre of the passband.

The circuit is basically just an operational amplifier used as an inverting amplifier having unity voltage gain set by the two feedback resistors, R1 and R4. However, the required bandpass filtering is provided by three additional components in the feedback network, and these are C4, C5 and Tr1. Tr1 is used here as a voltage controlled resistor, and R5 is used in series with Tr1 to effectively limit its minimum resistance to 1k. A bipolar transistor does not give good linearity when used as a voltage controlled resistor, and it is this that gives a significant amount of distortion when Tr1 is biased into conduction. The filter is at its minimum frequency when the input voltage is at about 0.5 volts, and the maximum frequency is achieved with the input potential at about 4.5 volts. The frequency range of the filter can obviously be changed by altering the value of C4 and C5 if necessary.

This bandpass filter arrangement is really just a variation on the arrangement shown in Figure 32 and described earlier, as will probably be apparent if the two circuits are compared.

Chapter 3

MISCELLANEOUS CIRCUITS

Comparators and trigger circuits are used in numerous applicat
and these very simple circuits are amongst the most useful
building blocks. The two basic types of comparator are the no
inverting and inverting types, and these are shown in the circu
diagrams of Figure 42(a) and (b) respectively. Special compar
integrated circuits are available, but in most cases it is cheaper
to use an operational amplifier as a voltage comparator, and
that is the technique used in the circuits described here.

An operational amplifier amplifies the voltage difference
across its two inputs, and at low frequencies the gain of these
devices is extremely high being typically about 100000 or
200000 times. Thus only a very small voltage difference
(typically only a fraction of a millivolt) is needed in order to
send the output fully positive or negative. The output goes
positive if the non-inverting input is the one at the higher
potential, or negative if the inverting input is the one at the
higher voltage.

In the circuit of Figure 42(a) the inverting input of IC1 is
biased to about half the supply voltage by R1 and R2. C1
decouples any noise which might be picked up at the invertin
input of IC1 and which might otherwise give unreliable result
from the circuit. If the non-inverting input is taken marginal
above the bias voltage fed to the inverting input the output o
IC1 goes high, and if the non-inverting input is taken fractior
below this bias potential the output of IC1 goes low.

The bias voltage fed to the inverting input does not have t
be half the supply voltage, and it can be any potential betwe
the two supply rail potentials. It does not have to be supplie
by a potential divider circuit either, and a zener shunt stabili
circuit could, for example, be used instead if this would give
better results for some reason.

The inverting version is essentially the same, but the bias
voltage is fed to the non-inverting input and the input voltag

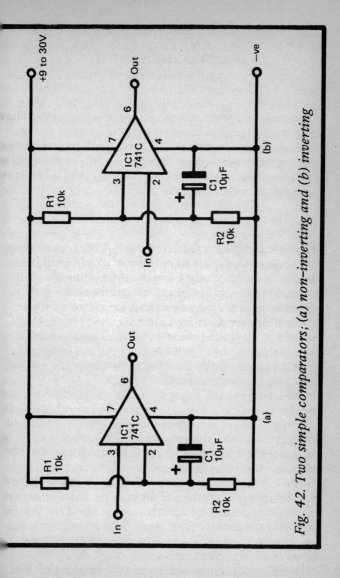

Fig. 42. Two simple comparators; (a) non-inverting and (b) inverting

applied to the inverting input. The output therefore goes low if the input is taken above the bias potential, or high if it is tak below this potential.

Using a 741C in the IC1 position it is important to rememb that the output voltage with the output in the low state is abo two volts or so above the negative supply potential. The outpu is about one volt below the positive supply voltage when it is i the high state. It is not usually difficult to interface the 741C to subsequent circuitry such as a LED indicator or relay driver but a CA3140E can be used instead of the 741C if it would be more convenient to have an output potential of virtually zero volts with the output in the low state.

Triggers

The simple comparator circuits of Figure 42 can sometimes gi unsatisfactory results due to the narrow range of input voltage that give an output voltage between the two extremes. With the input in this narrow range of voltages the output will not simply assume some intermediate output voltage since there will be a considerable amount of output noise with the operational amplifier effectively used as an open loop amplifi There is also a distinct possibility that noise picked up at the input will appear greatly amplified at the output and the circu could even be slightly unstable.

The solution to this problem is to use a trigger circuit whic is really just a slightly modified comparator circuit. Figure 4. shows the circuit of a simple inverting trigger circuit. R1 and R2 bias the non-inverting input to about half the supply volta but due to the inclusion of R3 this bias voltage is always modified under quiescent conditions. If IC1's output is high R3 is effectively connected in parallel and the bias voltage is increased to about one third of the supply voltage. When IC output is low the bias voltage is reduced to about one third o the supply voltage since R3 is then effectively connected in parallel with R2. If we assume that the output of IC1 is low, the inverting input must be taken below one third of the sup voltage in order to trigger the output to the high state. The inverting input only has to be taken low enough in potential

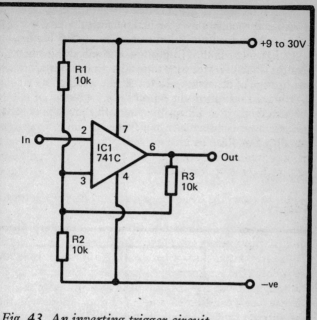

Fig. 43. An inverting trigger circuit

tart the output moving positive, since the positive feedback
hrough R3 then causes the output to almost instantly switch
o the high state. It is then necessary for the inverting input to
e taken above two thirds of the supply voltage in order to send
he output back to the low state, and again positive feedback
nsures that the output triggers straight from one output state
o the other and cannot take up a state between the two extremes.

An obvious effect of the positive feedback, apart from the
iggering of the output from one state to the other, is the
ntroduction of two distinct input voltages at which the circuit
witches output states. In this case there is a large amount of
edback through R2 and R3 so that the two voltages are well
parated. In some applications this would not be acceptable,
d R3 would have to be made much higher in value so that its

shunting effect on R1 and R2 would be greatly diminished. A value of 1 Megohm or even more should ensure reliable triggering from one state to the other, but where practical it is advisable to use a large amount of feedback as this will give the best possible reliability with good immunity to spurious operation due to noise or instability. Note that the effect of R3 will be slightly less than one might expect since the output of IC1 does not go fully positive or negative, and with a low supply voltage this will in fact substantially reduce the amount of hysteresis introduced by R3.

Non-Inverting Trigger

Figure 44 shows the circuit diagram of a non-inverting trigger,

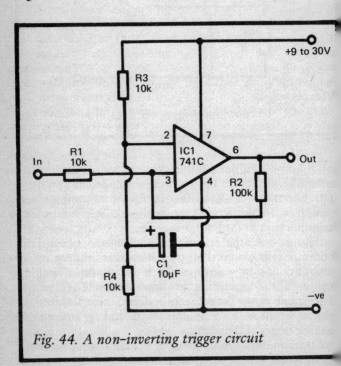

Fig. 44. A non-inverting trigger circuit

and like the inverting trigger circuit this one uses positive
feedback to give the triggering. Also as before, the input voltage
at which the output triggers to the high state becomes different
to the one at which it triggers back to the low state. In this case
it is a potential divider action across R1 and R2 that introduces
the hysteresis, and the degree of hysteresis can be controlled
changing the value of R2 as necessary.

AC Trigger

Trigger circuits are often used to convert sinewave or triangular
waveforms to a squarewave signal, and can also be used to process
a signal which has a high noise content to produce a squarewave
output that is free from noise and spurious pulses. It is the
hysteresis which gives this immunity and a large amount of
hysteresis is desirable in this application. Another feature of
trigger circuits of this type which can often be useful is that an
inadequate input level results in no output signal. This can be
used to advantage where a circuit of some kind will malfunction
and give unreliable results if it receives an inadequate signal level.
A trigger used ahead of such a circuit ensures that it either
receives a proper input signal or no input signal at all, and the
equipment therefore simply fails to operate rather than giving
misleading results.

Figure 45 shows the circuit diagram of a trigger circuit which
has AC coupling at the input. This circuit has obvious similarities
to the trigger circuit of Figure 43 which was described earlier,
and the main differences are the biasing of the inverting input
provided by R1 and R2, and the AC input coupling obtained by
using C1 at the input.

Using a 9 volt supply the circuit requires an input signal of
about 2 volts peak to peak or more in order to produce an
output signal, but the sensitivity of the circuit reduces roughly
in proportion to increases in the supply voltage. The sensitivity
of the circuit can be considerably boosted if necessary by
reducing the value of R5, but this also reduces the hysteresis and
noise immunity of the circuit.

The NE531N device specified for IC1 has a high slew-rate
and therefore gives a good quality squarewave output having a

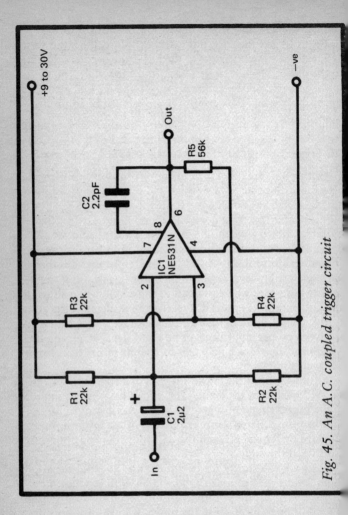

Fig. 45. An A.C. coupled trigger circuit

fast risetime. This may not be an important factor in some applications, and a 741C device can then be used in the IC1 position. C2 is a discrete compensation capacitor and is not required if a 741C is used for IC1.

80

Window Discriminator

The window discriminator circuit of Figure 46 produces a low output unless the input voltage falls within certain limits. Using the values shown for R1 to R3 the output is low unless the input voltage is between one third and two thirds of the supply voltage. However, by changing the values of R1 to R3 these limits can be set at any desired level. The lower limit is equal to the voltage fed to the non-inverting input of IC1b (pin 3) and the upper limit is equal to the voltage supplied to the inverting input of IC1a (pin 6). The two reference voltages can be set using separate potential dividers if preferred, or zener shunt stabiliser circuits can be used to provide these potentials. However, the higher reference voltage must always be applied to pin 6 of IC1 or the circuit will fail to operate properly.

Flip-Flop

Figure 47 shows the circuit diagram of a simple flip-flop or bistable circuit which uses a 555 (or the CMOS 7555 version of the 555) timer integrated circuit. These two devices were covered at some length in "Practical Electronic Building Blocks Book 1" and they will therefore not be described in detail again here.

Basically the circuit is just a standard 555 monostable, and the output can be triggered to the high state by taking pin 2 below one third of the supply voltage, and reset to the low state by taking pin 4 to less than about 0.5 volts. Normally an R − C timing network coupled to pins 6 and 7 of the 555 would determine the length of time that the output would remain in the high state if no reset pulse is provided before the end of this timing period. In this circuit though, the timing components are omitted and once triggered the output remains high for an indefinite period, and can only be returned to the low state by a reset pulse to pin 4 of IC1.

Once the circuit has been triggered it would be possible for stray pick-up at pins 6 and 7 to cause these pins to go above two thirds of the supply voltage, which would effectively be the same as a timing network reaching the end of the timing period

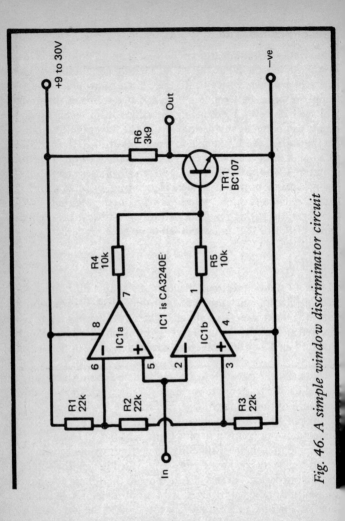

Fig. 46. A simple window discriminator circuit

and resetting the device. No problems of this type have been experienced by the author when using this circuit, and it is something that would probably only occur in a field of strong electrical interference. However, if spurious operation of this type should prove to be troublesome it should be possible to

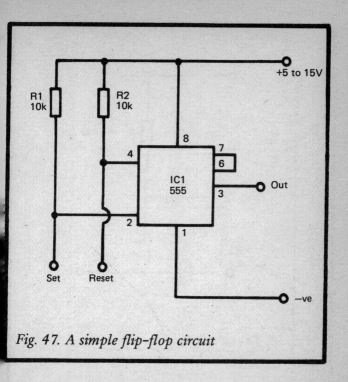

Fig. 47. A simple flip-flop circuit

remedy the problem by connecting a resistor of a few hundred kilohms in value from pins 6 and 7 of IC1 to the negative supply rail, or simply linking these pins to the negative supply rail.

The set and reset pulses can be provided in a number of ways, such as using mechanical switches to connect these inputs to the negative supply rail, or using common emitter connected transistors to pull the inputs down to suitable voltages when they receive positive input pulses.

Mixers

The mixer circuit of Figure 48 is ridiculously simple, but is useful in circuits where there are two signals which must be mixed together in the appropriate proportions. If we assume

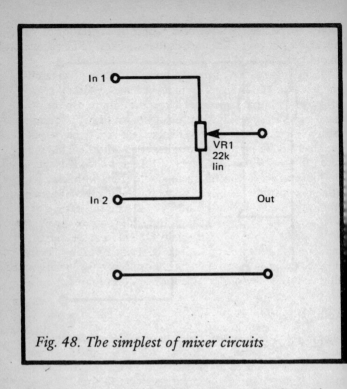

Fig. 48. The simplest of mixer circuits

that both input signals have the same source impedance, there
will be the same gain from each input to the output when the
wiper of VR1 is at the centre of its track. In fact as this is a
passive circuit it is more accurate to say that the losses from
each input to the output will be the same, and will be 6dB.
However, the load impedance at the output will increase these
losses, and will do so substantially if a low load impedance is
present. In some applications it may therefore be necessary to
use a buffer amplifier or a low gain voltage amplifier at the
output to minimise and compensate for the losses in the mixer
circuit. If the source impedances are not equal it simply mean
that balance will be achieved with the slider of VR1 off-centre
In an extreme case where one signal is from a high impedance
source and the other is from a low or medium impedance one

would not be possible to achieve balance at any setting of VR1, but this is not a set of conditions that are likely to be encountered in practice.

If the wiper of VR1 is moved towards the top of its track there is a lower impedance from input 1 to the output and effectively a higher impedance across the output. On the other hand as far as input 2 is concerned there is a higher impedance path to the output, and a lower impedance across the output terminals. Thus input 1 receives less attenuation and input 2 receives more. Taking the wiper of VR1 down towards the bottom end of its track has the opposite effect with less attenuation from input 2 to the output and more attenuation from very low source impedances, at the extreme settings of VR1 there will be no attenuation from one input to the output while the other input will be totally cut off from the output. If the source impedances are each in the region of a few kilohms the control range of the circuit will obviously only be fairly small, although still quite sufficient in the majority of cases.

Active Mixer

Figure 49 shows the circuit diagram of a basic operational amplifier active mixer, and this is a well known and much used configuration. The circuit is really just a form of inverting amplifier, but there are two input resistors (R1 and R2) with one input signal coupled to each resistor. The output therefore has to counteract the sum of the two input voltages (this mode of operation is sometimes called the "summing mode"), and the required mixing action is obtained. VR1 and VR2 enable the two input signals to be mixed in any desired proportions, and there is a maximum gain of unity from each input to the output. However, if necessary the voltage gain of the circuit can be increased by raising the value of R5, just as would be the case for a normal operational amplifier inverting mode circuit. The input impedance of the circuit is about 50k or so.

Although the mixer is shown here as a two input type, using this configuration it is in fact possible to have any number of inputs. It is merely necessary to add an extra 100k input resistor, 20nF DC blocking capacitor, and 100k logarithmic potentio-

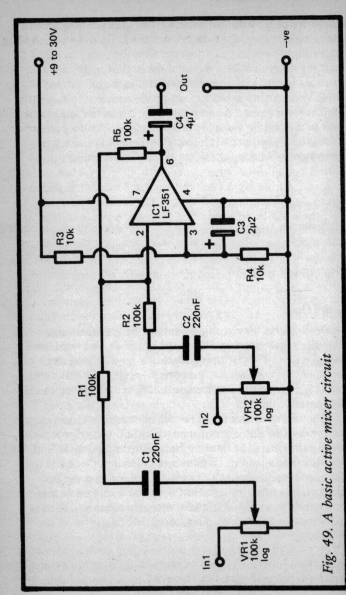

Fig. 49. A basic active mixer circuit

meter for each additional channel, with the extra components being connected in the same fashion as R1, C1 and VR1. Adding extra channels to the unit does not alter the performance of the existing channels in any way, and the level of performance at the extra inputs is the same as that at the original two inputs. In this respect this type of mixer circuit is superior to a passive circuit plus amplifier, as with the latter the gain of the circuit steadily reduces as extra channels are added. Another advantage of this configuration over a passive mixer is that there is no perceptible interaction between the level controls.

Simple Gates

It can sometimes be necessary to have a simple gate circuit which can be used to pass or cut off an audio signal of some kind, and Figure 50 shows the circuits of two very simple gate circuits of this type. If we consider Figure 50(a) first, with Tr1 switched off it has such a high collector to emitter impedance that it has no significant effect on the circuit, and the only losses through R1 are those caused by a potential divider action in conjunction with the load impedance at the output. If a control voltage of about 6 to 12 volts is applied to the circuit Tr1 is biased hard into conduction and it has a collector to emitter impedance of just a few ohms. This produces severe losses of almost 80dB through R1, and this is high enough to give no significant output signal.

The circuit of Figure 50(b) is not substantially different, and simply uses a VMOS transistor instead of a bipolar device plus input current limiting resistor. Note that the VN1OKM VMOS transistor has a built-in 15 volt zener protection diode and it does not therefore require any special handling precautions. However, the input voltage must not exceed 15 volts or this protection diode will be brought into conduction and a heavy input current could flow. This would probably result in the destruction of Tr1.

An electronic changeover switching action can be obtained by using two gate circuits with their outputs feeding into a mixer circuit (such as the circuit of Figure 48 or the one of Figure 49).

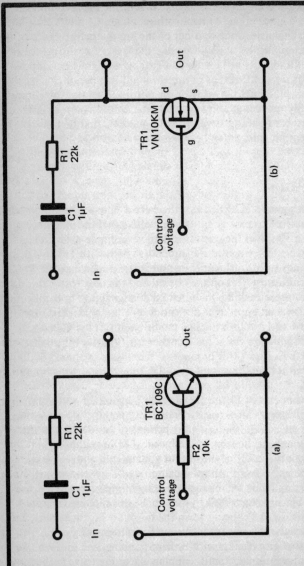

Fig. 50. Two simple audio gate circuits

88

The control inputs of the two gates must be operated out-of-phase (i.e. when one control voltage is high the other must be low) so that only one or other of the input signals is fed through to the output.

Clipping Amplifier

In most applications it is necessary for amplifiers to have a reasonably high degree of linearity in order to obtain satisfactory results, but there are occasions when a non-linear amplifier of some kind is needed. The most simple of non-linear amplifiers is the clipping type, and this is simply an amplifier which operates in a linear fashion until the input signal voltage reaches a certain level, and the gain of the circuit then reduces so that as the input voltage increases the output voltage remains virtually static. This effect can, of course, be obtained by overloading a linear amplifier, and this is a method of clipping which is sometimes used in practical circuits. It can often be more satisfactory to use a clipping amplifier of the type shown in Figure 51 though, and this is based on an inverting mode operational amplifier circuit. R1 and R4 set the input impedance and gain of the circuit at 10k and 20dB (10 times) respectively, but these can be modified to suit individual requirements by giving these two components the appropriate values.

The clipping is introduced by D1 and D2, and these are not biased into conduction and have no significant effect on the circuit unless the output signal reaches about 1.2 volts peak to peak. These diodes are then biased into conduction on signal peaks, and shunt R4 during the periods of conduction so that the voltage gain of the circuit is reduced. The impedance of D1 and D2 reduces sharply as the output voltage rises above ± 0.6 volts, and the reduction in gain this causes is sufficient to ensure that only a small increase in output voltage is produced even if the input signal voltage is taken well above the clipping threshold. D1 provides the clipping when the output is positive going, and D2 gives the clipping when the output is negative going.

This arrangement gives very hard clipping, and some applications require "soft" clipping where increases in the input

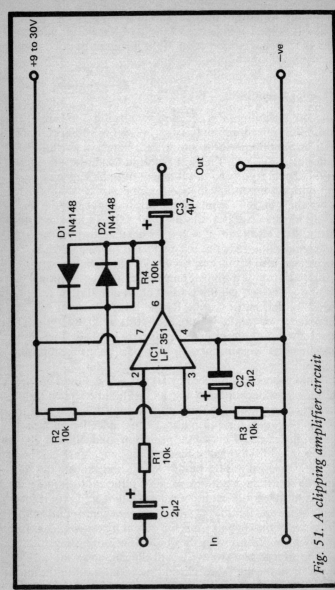

Fig. 51. A clipping amplifier circuit

+9 to 30V

−ve

D1
1N4148

D2
1N4148

R4
100k

C3
4µ7

Out

7

6

4

IC1
LF 351

2

3

C2
2µ2

R2
10k

R1
10k

R3
10k

C1
2µ2

In

90

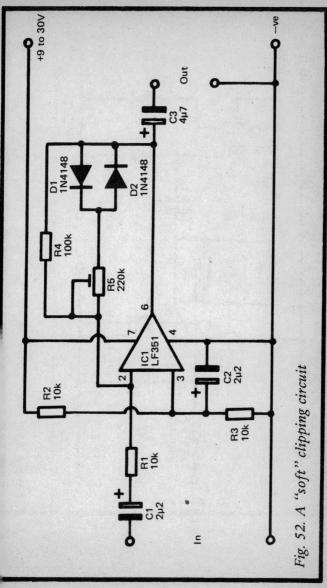

Fig. 52. A "soft" clipping circuit

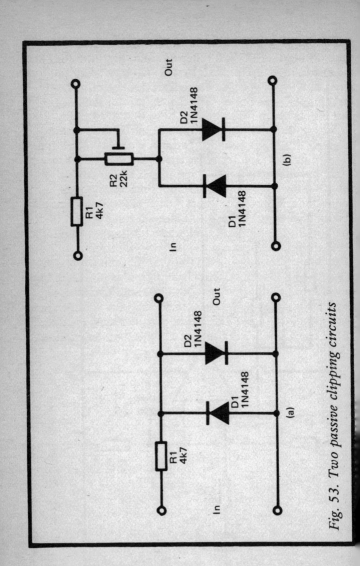

Fig. 53. Two passive clipping circuits

signal voltage do give a small but significant increase in the output voltage. This "soft" clipping can be obtained using the modified circuit of Figure 52. Here R5 has been added in series with two clipping diodes to limit their effect, and the higher the effective value of R5 the "softer" the limiting that is obtained.

Simple passive clipping circuits are sometimes all that is required, and Figure 53 shows two simple circuits of this type. Figure 53(a) is a "hard" limiting circuit and Figure 53(b) is a "soft" clipping circuit. These operate in a similar fashion to the active circuits with the diodes not being brought into conduction and having no effect if the input voltage is less than about 1.2 volts peak to peak. At higher input levels the diodes conduct during signal peaks and produce increased losses through R1 so that the required clipping is obtained.

By using germanium diodes (such as OA90s or OA91s) in the circuit of Figure 53(a) the clipping threshold is reduced to only a few tens of millivolts peak to peak, and the intensity of the clipping steadily increases as the input signal is raised above the clipping threshold. This gives a very interesting form of "soft" clipping which can be very useful in some applications.

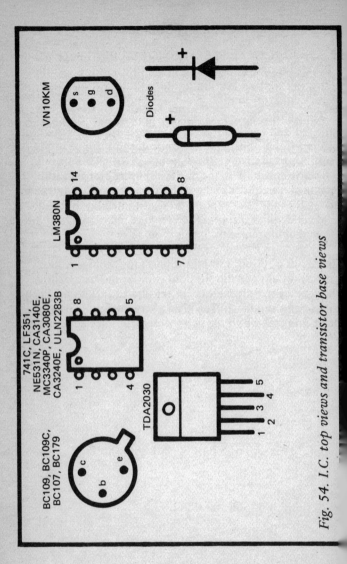

Fig. 54. I.C. top views and transistor base views

94

IN THE SAME SERIES

BP117: PRACTICAL ELECTRONIC BUILDING BLOCKS – BOOK 1
R. A. Penfold

Written in the same style as this book and designed to complement it, Book 1 covers in general signal generating circuits.

Chapter 1 deals with a number of different oscillator circuits, covering most of the output waveforms that are ever likely to be needed by the hobbyist, and covering a frequency range of less than 1 Hertz to many Megahertz.

Oscillator circuits are used in a surprisingly large number of electronic projects including such diverse pieces of equipment as radio transmitters and receivers, test equipment, musical effects units and model train controllers.

Chapter 2 covers monostable multi-vibrators, that is circuits that when triggered by an input signal of some kind produce a single output pulse of a certain duration. Circuits of this type are used in timers, switch debouncers and many other applications.

Chapter 3 includes a number of miscellaneous circuits such as noise generators, rectifier circuits, power supplies, regulators and latches etc.

28 pages   *1983*
85934 092 9   **£1.95**

OTHER BOOKS OF INTEREST

BP53: PRACTICAL ELECTRONICS CALCULATIONS AND FORMULAE
F. A. Wilson, C.G.I.A., C.Eng., F.I.E.E., F.I.E.R.E., F.B.I.M.

This book has been written, not for the family bookshelf, but for the electronic enthusiast's workshop bench. Its aim is to bridge the gap between complicated technical theory, which sometimes seems to have little relevance to practical work and "cut-and-dried" methods which may bring success in design but leave the experimenter unfulfilled.

There is, therefore, a strong practical bias — tedious and higher mathematics have been avoided where possible and many tables have been included, partly to save calculation and partly because actual figures bring a greater intimacy with the design process.

Yet for those who, in technical studies have found difficulty, or in common with most other people have lapses of memory, there is plenty of help and revision.

As a reference book, sections have been written to be as self contained as possible. The book is divided into six basic sections: Units and Constants, Direct-current Circuits, Passive Components, Alternating current Circuits, Networks and Theorems, Measurements.

256 pages   1979
0 900162 70 8   £2.95

BP80: POPULAR ELECTRONIC CIRCUITS – BOOK 1
R. A. Penfold

Another book by the very popular author, Mr Penfold, who has designed and developed a large number of various circuits which are accompanied by a short text giving a brief introduction, circuit description and any special notes on construction and setting-up that may be necessary.

The circuits are grouped together under the following headings Audio Circuits, Radio Circuits, Test Gear Circuits, Music Project Circuits, Household Project Circuits and Miscellaneous Circuits.

An extremely useful book for all electronic hobbyists, offering remarkable value for the number of designs that it contains. Also see book number BP98.

160 pages   198
0 85934 055 4   £1.9

BP98: POPULAR ELECTRONIC CIRCUITS – BOOK 2
R. A. Penfold

Like *Popular Electronic Circuits – Book 1* (BP80), this book provides wide range of designs for electronics enthusiasts who are capable of producing working projects from just a circuit diagram without the ai of detailed constructional information. However, many of the projec are fairly simple and straightforward and should not prove beyond th capabilities of constructors who have only a limited amount of experience. Where relevant, any special setting-up procedures are described.

The circuits cover a wide range of subjects and are all based on modern, inexpensive components. Most of the circuits are for devices that, when completed, form projects in their own right. Some are intended as electronic building-blocks for use in larger projects or systems, and a few fall in both categories. None of the designs in this book duplicate those in Book 1.

160 pages   *1982*
0 85934 073 2   £2.25

BP88: HOW TO USE OP AMPS
E. A. Parr, B.Sc., C.Eng., M.I.E.E.

The operational amplifier is probably the most versatile IC available to the electronics engineer. For a price similar to a general purpose transistor, it is possible to purchase an IC with several hundred "components", very high gain and predictable performance. The Op Amp is thus a basic building-block for applications from audio to industrial control.

This book has been written as a designer's guide covering many operational amplifiers, serving both as a source book of circuits and a reference book for design calculations. The approach has been made as non-mathematical as possible and it is hoped, easily understandable by most readers, be they engineers or hobbyists.

The text is divided into the following main chapters: Meet the Operational Amplifier, Basic Circuits, Oscillators, Audio Circuits, Filters, Miscellaneous Circuits, Common Op Amps, Power Supplies, Constructional Notes and Fault-finding.

160 pages   *1982*
0 85934 063 5   £2.25

Notes

Notes

Notes

Notes

Notes

Please note overleaf is a list of other titles that are available in our range of Radio, Electronics and Computer Books.

These should be available from all good Booksellers, Radio Component Dealers and Mail Order Companies.

However, should you experience difficulty in obtaining any title in your area, then please write directly to the publisher enclosing payment to cover the cost of the book plus adequate postage.

If you would like a complete catalogue of our entire range of Radio, Electronics and Computer Books then please send a Stamped Addressed Envelope to:

BERNARD BABANI (publishing) LTD
THE GRAMPIANS
SHEPHERDS BUSH ROAD
LONDON W6 7NF
ENGLAND